45 SIMPLE EL
BLOC

Other Titles of Interest

45 SIMPLE ELECTRONIC TERMINAL BLOCK PROJECTS

by

ROY BEBBINGTON, MISTC

**BERNARD BABANI (publishing) LTD
THE GRAMPIANS
SHEPHERDS BUSH ROAD
LONDON W6 7NF
ENGLAND**

Please Note

Although every care has been taken with the production of this book to ensure that any projects, designs, modifications and/or programs, etc., contained herewith, operate in a correct and safe manner and also that any components specified are normally available in Great Britain, the Publishers do not accept responsibility in any way for the failure, including fault in design, of any project, design, modification or program to work correctly or to cause damage to any other equipment that it may be connected to or used in conjunction with, or in respect of any other damage or injury that may be so caused, nor do the Publishers accept responsibility in any way for the failure to obtain specified components.

Notice is also given that if equipment that is still under warranty is modified in any way or used or connected with home-built equipment then that warranty may be void.

First Published – October 1995

British Library Cataloguing in Publication Data
Bebbington, R.
   45 Simple Electronic Terminal Block Projects
   1. Title
   621.381

ISBN 0 85934 378 2

Printed and bound in Great Britain by Cox & Wyman Ltd, Reading

Preface

When soldering is a 'NO GO AREA!' for youngsters and beginners in electronics, a practical solution is a series of simple projects that can be built on screw-terminal blocks. This type of plastic terminal block is widely used by electricians and often referred to as a 'chocolate block' – some resemblance, but quite tasteless! Another essential safety feature for beginners is that all projects must be powered by nothing more harmful than a small battery. All forty-five projects in this book satisfy these requirements.

Armed with a layout diagram showing the actual physical shape of the components and instructions, most projects can be constructed within a matter of minutes. A small list of components is found at the end of each project, made up from a nucleus of common items, allowing them to be re-used for many other projects. Most circuits can be easily modified for experimentation, or extended as modular units. Since the wire ends do not have to be cut and soldered, components can be used again and again.

For ease of construction, the projects mainly use discrete wire-ended components, such as resistors, capacitors, diodes, transistors, etc. Typically, battery supplies and holders are fitted with wire-ended clips. However, components that are not wire-ended, for example potentiometers, loudspeakers, thyristors, etc., can be wire-wrapped, or better still, enlist the services of a friend with a soldering iron to add connecting leads. Short, flexible leads soldered to these few components will pay dividends when you come to connect them into the terminal block projects.

As the book is aimed at younger readers and beginners, simplified instructions are given for those not familiar with electrical and electronic components and circuits.

All the projects are essentially practical and consist of useful household gadgets, test equipment, simple musical devices, games, etc., under such chapter headings as Sound and Music, Entertainment, Test & Measuring. Each project is numbered from 1 to 45 for easy reference.

In addition to the block wiring layout showing physical components and connections, the circuit diagram is included to familiarise readers with components symbols and circuit conventions.

Roy Bebbington

Contents

Page

Chapter 1

CONNECTIONS AND COMPONENTS

To construct an electronic project on screw-type terminal blocks without it resembling a bird's nest, it is better to keep the number of components and connections to a minimum. With this in mind, these projects have been restricted to relatively simple, though interesting circuits, using a basic kit of parts applicable for several projects, and adding extra components where required. As the screw-in method of construction does not mutilate the wire ends, components can easily be unscrewed, changed and used again for other projects.

Connections

Some of the components listed, for instance potentiometers and loudspeakers, are not wire-ended so it is necessary when gathering the kit together to add short lengths of wire to these to make terminal block connections. There are only a few exceptions so these modifications will not take many minutes. If you are not able to solder these yourself, then enlist the aid of a friend who is handy with a soldering iron. The alternative is to wire-wrap these connections. This can usually be done easily as potentiometers, speakers, transformers, etc., often have terminal lugs with small holes in them to secure the connecting wires. Other components such as lamp holders and switches often have miniature screw terminals to which small lengths of wire can be attached.

For connections in constant use, switches, speakers, etc., it is better to use stranded wire as this offers more flexibility. Where circuits require components in remote positions, for instance a remote speaker or door pushbutton, a small terminal block can be interposed to add extension leads. Insulated wires should always be used for long leads and where there is any possibility of bare wires touching together. Plastic sleeving can be fitted over any component ends to avoid potential short-circuits. Always make sure that the ends of the wires are stripped back to allow the screw terminals to grip the bare wire cleanly.

1

For some projects, you may find it easier to screw the terminal block (or blocks) on to a piece of plywood or block-board to provide a stable base for your layout. Your basic tools for wiring up the circuits for these projects are a pair of wire-strippers, side-cutters and a small screwdriver suitable for the screws in the terminal block.

Introducing Components

Batteries (BY1 ...)
Low-voltage batteries provide the electrical energy for all the projects in this book. The higher the supply voltage, the more electrons the battery can force around the circuit. Most of the circuits operate quite happily on a 9-volt layer-battery such as a PP3. The combination of battery-powered circuits and sol-derless connections means that the projects can be built by the young or inexperienced constructor with safety.

Buzzers (WD1 ...)
A miniature solid-state buzzer, operating at 6V provides a 400Hz, 75dB output at 30cm. The output leads are red (+) and black (–) and must be appropriately connected (see Project 1).

Capacitors (C1 ...)
Capacitors store electrical energy. Various values are used in these projects to store charges (e.g. Project 15), give time delay, to block signals or sometimes to tune them in. Although the unit of capacitance is the farad, we think of a hundred micro-farads ($100\mu F$) as a large capacitor. Most capacitors of one microfarad ($1\mu F$) and over are polarised (+ and –), and are known as electrolytic capacitors and must be connected in cir-cuit the correct way round. The values of smaller capacitors are given in nF (nanofarads) and pF (picofarads). For example, $0.01\mu F = 10nF = 10,000pF$. Unless electrolytic or otherwise indicated, all capacitors for the projects in this book should be polystyrene, metallised polyester film or mylar film.

Variable Capacitors (VC1 ...)
Variable capacitors are used for tuning purposes, for example in the receivers, Projects 31 and 32. They consist of parallel metal

plates with a dielectric such as air in between. The plates can be interleaved by rotating the control knob. As the plates are meshed, the area of overlap is increased and the distance between them decreased, so increasing the capacity. Typical values are 500 picofarad maximum.

Coils or Inductors (L1 ...)

These devices that tend to prevent a change of current, are often used with capacitors for tuned circuits or filters in radios or in oscillator circuits (for example, see Project 3). The unit of inductance is the henry (H) or millihenry (mH) and depends on the number of turns and the core material.

Diodes (D1 ...)

Diodes pass current in one direction only, so must also be connected the correct way round. The cathode end (k) is distinguished from the anode (a) by a wide band. They are used for various purposes: to rectify alternating currents, to detect radio frequency signals, to block signals and to protect circuits from surge currents.

Light-emitting diodes (D1 ...)

Light-emitting diodes (LEDs) operate like normal diodes, but give off light when an electric current flows through them. Light-emitting diodes are available in four colours: red, green, yellow and orange, and must be connected the right way round in a circuit. The forward voltage of 2V and forward current of 20mA should not be exceeded. Higher supply voltages for LEDs can be reduced by using a limiting resistor in series.

Light-dependent resistor (PCC1 ...)

Light-dependent resistors, or photo-conductive cells like the ORP12 cadmium sulphide cell, are sensing devices that respond to visible light in a similar way to the human eye. The resistance of the cell varies from tens of ohms in bright sunlight to several megohms in total darkness. This change of resistance can be used in circuits for automatically controlling security lights, counting and burglar alarms.

Loudspeakers (LS1 ...)

A miniature loudspeaker with a 64-ohm impedance voice coil is suitable for direct single-transistor drive. It is listed for all the audio projects and can also be used as a microphone in a pre-amplifier circuit.

Resistors (R1 ...)

Resistors are measured in ohms and are used to control currents and voltages in a circuit. The values range from less than one ohm to several million ohms and are colour-coded, usually by three bands at one end. In case you get your resistors mixed, here is the code:

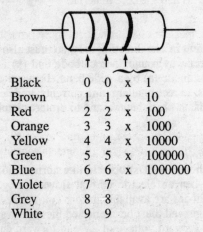

Black	0	0	x	1
Brown	1	1	x	10
Red	2	2	x	100
Orange	3	3	x	1000
Yellow	4	4	x	10000
Green	5	5	x	100000
Blue	6	6	x	1000000
Violet	7	7		
Grey	8	8		
White	9	9		

The tolerance (how accurate the value of the resistor is) is normally indicated by a fourth band, Gold ± 5%; Silver ± 10%. For example, in Project 2, the first three colour bands of resistor R1 are red (2), violet (7) and orange (3), denoting (2)(7)(000) ohms. On the diagram, this is referred to as 27k, i.e. twenty-seven thousand ohms. Similarly, a million ohms is referred to as 1M (1,000,000 ohms). Unless otherwise indicated all resistors used in the projects in this book should be ¼ watt, 10%.

Potentiometers (VR1 ...)

In addition to the fixed resistors, variable carbon track resistors known as potentiometers or 'pots' are used in some projects, for instance, to vary the oscillator speed as in the gliding slide (Project 5), or the metronome (Project 10). Variable resistors are also used in some meter projects to adjust zero or full-scale deflection. In these applications only the middle (the wiper or slider) and one outer connection are needed. However, where a potential divider is needed all three connections are used. For instance, the wiper taps off part of a voltage to the meter in Project 40 and a potential divider is also used to find the null point in the capacitance bridge of Project 42. Linear (lin) potentiometers are preferred in these projects, i.e. equal rotation gives equal resistance changes. Logarithmic (log) ones have most of the adjustment all at one end.

Switches (S1 ...)
Several switch types are used throughout these projects:
- the pushbutton switch, locking or non-locking,with screw type connections (e.g. as in in Project 1);
- the single-pole, single-throw (S.P.S.T.) slide switch, often used as an on/off switch;
- the single-pole, double-throw (S.P.D.T.) microswitch (e.g. in Project 3);
- the single-pole, 4-way rotary switch in Project 19;
- the reed switch consists of a pair of contacts controlled by an external magnet (e.g. in Project 16).

Terminal blocks (TB1 ...)
12-way, flexible, terminal block strips in moulded plastic are widely available in DIY stores under electrical accessories. Both 2A and 5A sizes are suitable, the narrower spacing between terminals of the 2A strips being especially useful for components with short connecting leads. These strips can easily be cut into shorter lengths as required with a junior hacksaw.

Thyristors (Thy1 ...)
A thyristor, or silicon-controlled rectifier, is a semiconductor device used to switch a heavy current from anode to cathode when a small trigger current is applied to the gate electrode (see Projects 20, 22, 23, 26).

Transformers (T1 ...)
Transformers are alternating current (a.c.) devices, useful for

coupling purposes, to isolate circuits or to step-up or step-down voltages in a circuit.

Transistors (TR1 ...)

These are active components, three-legged devices that can be connected to amplify, to switch signals, or to provide oscillation. The BC108/BC109 transistor used for most of these projects is an npn type, so its collector is wired positive with respect to its emitter.

Chapter 2

SOUND AND MUSIC

This chapter covers a number of audio circuits, loosely grouped as sound and music projects. Although 'chocolate block' construction imposes some limitations, all these circuits have practical applications and many are capable of expansion to more advanced projects.

Project 1 – Simple Morse Code Practice Unit

This project serves as a gentle lead-in if you are a newcomer to building electronic circuits. For this reason, although the circuit is simple, it is explained in some detail to enable beginners to grasp the relationship between a theoretical circuit and its practical realisation.

Layout (Fig.1.1)

The layout diagram lists the five components, shows what they look like physically, and how they are wired up on a terminal block to form a circuit.

The connections between the 6-way terminal block TB1 and the components have been drawn as short as possible for convenience. However, it is better to leave a generous length of lead on components, especially if you want to use them again for other projects. In Figure 1.1, for instance, you might like to add a remote switch (S2) for another operator, connected by a pair of long wires to TB1.1 and TB1.2.

Notice that three components in this project have to be fitted the correct way round for it to work – D1, WD1, and the battery clip. The positive leads of WD1 and the battery clip are easily identified as red, the negative leads are black. However, the polarity of D1, the light-emitting diode (LED) is not so obvious. Generally, the cathode is the shorter lead and is also adjacent to a flat edge on the side of the plastic casing – but not always! Fortunately, it is easy to make sure by connecting up a test circuit as follows: loop a 1 kilohm (1000 ohms) resistor in

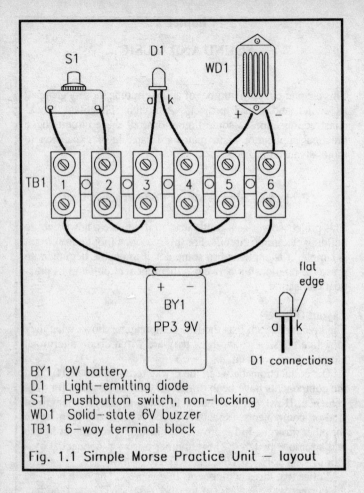

BY1   9V battery
D1   Light—emitting diode
S1   Pushbutton switch, non—locking
WD1   Solid—state 6V buzzer
TB1   6—way terminal block

Fig. 1.1 Simple Morse Practice Unit — layout

series with the LED and a 9V battery. If the LED fails to light, reverse the LED connections. With the LED on, its connection towards the positive of the battery is the anode (a) and the other connection towards the negative of the battery is the cathode (k). Alternatively, wire up the circuit of Figure 1.1, fit the battery and press S1. If nothing happens then reverse the LED connections on TB1.3 and TB1.4.

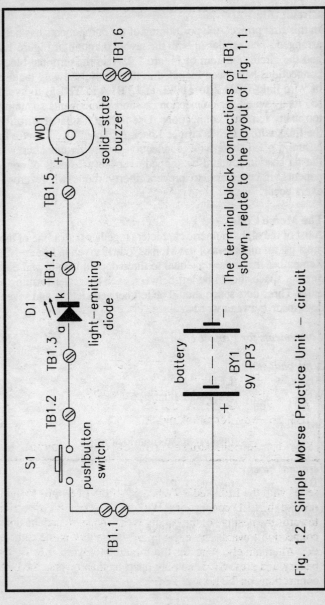

Fig. 1.2 Simple Morse Practice Unit – circuit

The terminal block connections of TB1 shown, relate to the layout of Fig. 1.1.

9

Circuit (Fig.1.2)

In this first project, the positioning of the components has been arranged to be similar in both the layout diagram of Figure 1.1 and the circuit diagram of Figure 1.2. Also the terminal block connections have been included in the circuit, showing the use of wire links (TB1.2 to TB1.3, and TB1.4 to TB1.5) to avoid too many wires per connection or short components spanning too many terminal connections. Use plastic insulated wire for the links with the ends stripped back for about a centimetre to ensure a good 'bare-wire' connection by the terminal screws. Plastic sleeving should be slipped over the wire ends of components, if necessary, to prevent short-circuits where cross-overs occur.

The Morse Code

A list of the alpha-numeric characters together with some of the most useful messages of the Morse Code is given in Figure 1.3. Remember that a dash is equal to three dots in length, and that one dot space should be left between each character forming a letter. Three dots space should be left between letters and seven dots space between words.

Components for Project 1

Semiconductors
D1   LED
WD1   solid-state buzzer, 6V

Switches
S1   push to make (non-locking)

Terminal block
TB1   6-way

Miscellaneous
9V battery PP3 and clip wire links.

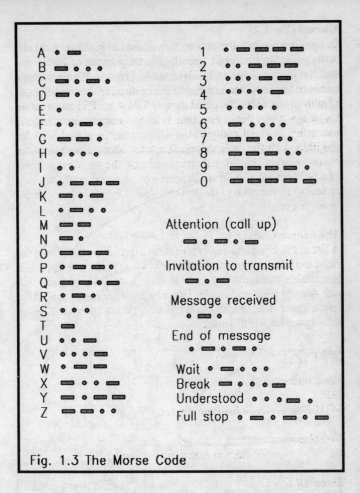

Fig. 1.3 The Morse Code

Project 2 – Audio/Visual Morse Sender

Here's a more sophisticated project that will enable you to send sound as well as light. Add an extension Morse key, and you can have a cosy (or is it a cody?) chat with a friend across a room. There are other interesting possibilities for remote communication using wire links, described later.

Principle

The project uses a transistor as a feedback amplifier to provide oscillation. The feedback principle is easy to understand, and one that you will be familiar with when public address systems are used, or misused. If the volume control on an amplifier is turned up too much, or the microphone faces, or is too near to the loudspeaker, then the system howls – goes into oscillation.

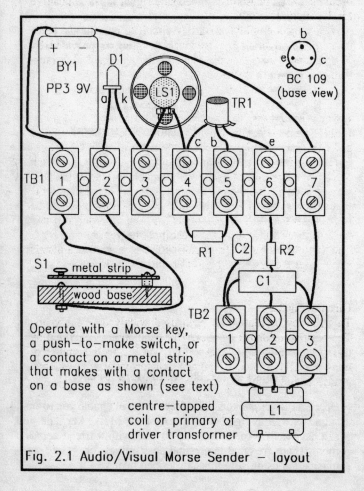

Operate with a Morse key, a push-to-make switch, or a contact on a metal strip that makes with a contact on a base as shown (see text)

centre-tapped coil or primary of driver transformer

Fig. 2.1 Audio/Visual Morse Sender – layout

What happens is that the sound from the loudspeaker is fed back into the microphone, amplified electrically again to the loudspeaker and 'heard' by the microphone as an even louder noise. So the 'music goes round and around' and creates a very loud howl. That is called acoustic feedback, but if we want to create electrical feedback we couple some of the output of an amplifier stage back to an input stage to provide a controlled oscillation. The phase of the feedback signal must be positive for the circuit to oscillate.

This project employs a Hartley circuit to provide the feedback for oscillation. The feedback coupling is provided by using a tapped coil. A centre-tapped winding on a driver transformer is shown in this case.

Layout (Fig.2.1)

In this layout, a smaller 3-way terminal block TB2 is used in addition to TB1 to provide connections for the coil L1. If preferred, one longer terminal block could be substituted. Switch S1 can be a standard Morse key if available instead of the DIY version shown. The pitch of the note will vary according to the inductance of the L1 coil. The value of capacitor C1 should be increased if the pitch of the note is too high, or reduced if it is too low. Remember to observe the polarity for D1 and BY1. The three lead-outs for transistor TR1 are as shown; a plastic sleeve over the base lead helps to avoid short-circuits.

Circuit (Fig.2.2)

This Hartley oscillator has been used widely over the years. The positive feedback necessary for oscillation is provided by taking the centre-tap of the coil L1, via R2, to the emitter of transistor TR1. If a centre-tapped transformer is not available, a suitable coil for L1 is described in Project 3.

Components for Project 2

Resistors

R1	27k
R2	150

13

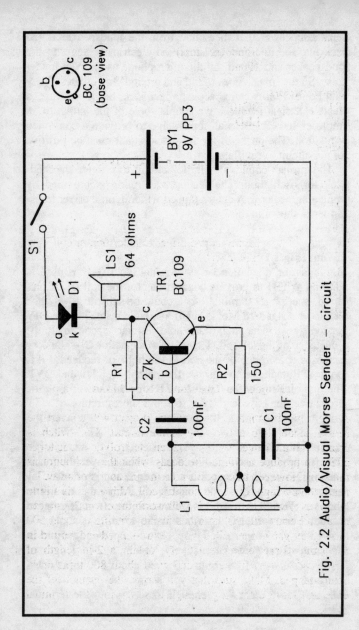

Fig. 2.2 Audio/Visual Morse Sender – circuit

Capacitors
C1   100nF (see text)
C2   100nF

Semiconductors
TR1   BC109
D1   LED

Switch
S1   push to make, non-locking (see text)

Loudspeaker
LS1   miniature 64 ohms

Coils
L1   centre-tapped driver transformer, or coil
              (see text)

Terminal Blocks
TB1   7-way
TB2   3-way

Miscellaneous
9V battery PP3 and clip wire links.

Project 3 – Two-Tone Door Chimes

A slight modification to the previous project will convert the
Morse sender into a two-tone chime circuit. The switch is
changed to a changeover type and an electrolytic capacitor is
added to produce a chime-like decay when the pushbutton is
released. However, to keep this note in tune as it dies away, L1
needs to be a high 'Q' (good quality) coil. Although it is a little
laborious to wind by hand it is well worth the effort. If you can
obtain a Ferroxcube pot core, a suitable winding is about 500
turns of 39-gauge enamelled wire, centre-tapped and **wound in
the same direction**. Alternatively, obtain a 2-in length of
ferrite rod as used for aerials and wind about 800 turns on it,
centre-tapped. Make sure that you scrape the enamel off the
ends and leave them long enough to screw into the terminal
block.

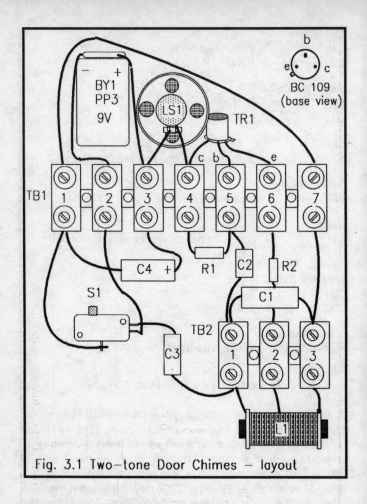

Fig. 3.1 Two-tone Door Chimes — layout

Layout (Fig.3.1)
The layout is similar to the previous project, but watch that some components have been interchanged, and a wire link has been introduced between TB1.1 and TB1.7. If a microswitch is not to hand, the circuit can be tried by making a DIY changeover switch from a 3-way terminal block and three short pieces of stiff wire suitably bent to shape.

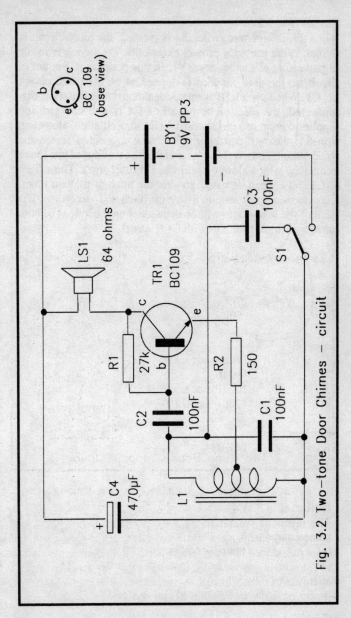

Fig. 3.2 Two-tone Door Chimes — circuit

17

Circuit (Fig.3.2)

When the changeover switch S1 is pressed, the basic circuit is similar to the previous project except that the switch is in the negative side of the battery BY1. In this position, C3 is not in circuit, so the note sounded is dependent on the tuned circuit L1, C1. When switch S1 is released, although the battery is disconnected, the electrolytic capacitor C4 is still charged and supplies current to keep transistor TR1 in oscillation. However, with S1 released, capacitor C3 is now connected across the tuned circuit, consequently a second note is produced at a lower frequency, which slowly decays as C4 discharges. The values of C1 and C3 can be varied to alter the pitch of the two tones. Increase the capacitance to lower the pitch and vice versa. The pitch of the lower note will be dependent on the values of both capacitors in parallel, i.e. with S1 released.

Components for Project 3

Resistors

R1	27k
R2	150

Capacitors

C1	100nF (see text)
C2	100nF
C3	100nF (see text)
C4	470µF elect. 10V

Semiconductors

TR1	BC109

Switch

S1	microswitch changeover, non-locking (see text)

Loudspeaker

LS1	miniature 64 ohms

Coils

L1	centre-tapped coil (see text)

Terminal Blocks
TB1   7-way
TB2.   3-way

Miscellaneous
9V battery PP3 and clip wire links.

Project 4 – Warning Bleeper

Here's a different oscillator, a slow-running circuit that is used
to switch a solid-state buzzer on and off at approximately one
second intervals. It can be used for several applications, for
example, as a contact-operated burglar alarm, or as a warning
bleeper operated by a single-throw switch, to attract attention
when the circuit is activated. This circuit, known as an astable
multivibrator, is the basis for several projects so it is useful to
know a little about it. Astable (not stable) means that it oscil-
lates continuously from one state to the other. You can regard it
as two resistance-capacity stages, one connected back into the
other to give positive feedback as described in Project 2. It produces rectangular-wave pulses at both transistor collectors,
which are rich in harmonics; these provide useful generators
for music circuits.

Layout (Fig.4.1)
While this project can be built on a 9-way terminal block, if
you are thinking of a rebuilding to take in the next two projects,
it will save time if you use a 10-way block. Remember, it is
advisable to use sleeving over the resistor and capacitor leads
to avoid short-circuits where the cross-overs occur.

Circuit (Fig.4.2)
The choice of capacitors C1, C2 and resistors R2, R3 determine
the rate at which the rectangular waveforms reverse. As shown,
the time period in seconds is approximately equal to $1.4 \times C1$
(farads) $\times R3$ (ohms) assuming $R2 = R3$ and $C1 = C2$. For some
applications where short pulses are required, the mark/space
ratio can be varied by choosing a different value for R2 and R3
and/or a different value for C1 and C2.

19

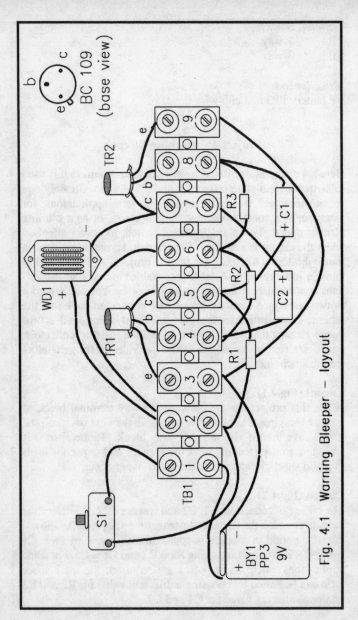

Fig. 4.1 Warning Bleeper – layout

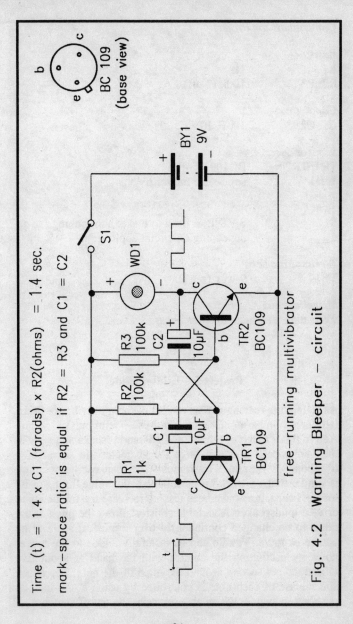

Time (t) = 1.4 × C1 (farads) × R2(ohms) = 1.4 sec.

mark-space ratio is equal if R2 = R3 and C1 = C2

Fig. 4.2 Warning Bleeper – circuit

free-running multivibrator

BY1
9V

BC 109
(base view)

Components for Project 4

Resistors
R1   1k
R2, R3   100k (2 off)

Capacitors
C1, C2   10µF, 10V (2 off)

Semiconductors
TR1, TR2   BC109 (2 off)
WD1   solid-state buzzer 6V

Switch
S1   S.P.S.T. or push to make, non-locking,
                  depending on circuit application

Terminal Block
TB1   9-way (see text)

Miscellaneous
9V battery PP3 and clip wire links.

Project 5 – Gliding Slide

As stated, the rectangular waveform of the multivibrator oscillator is rich in harmonics and so makes a useful musical sound. Add to this a touch of vibrato and glissando (shake and slide to the unmusical!) and you have the characteristic sound of a trombone – the author's instrument! The basic oscillator circuit is similar to the previous project but smaller value timing resistors and capacitors have been used to increase the frequency to drive a loudspeaker. A variable resistor allows the pitch of the notes to be changed continuously over a musical scale of an octave or more. Vibrato can be tastefully added to the longer notes by oscillating the control with the hand at about five vibrations per second around the pitch of the note. The attack and release of each note is controlled by using a non-locking pushbutton switch, which also serves as the on/off switch.

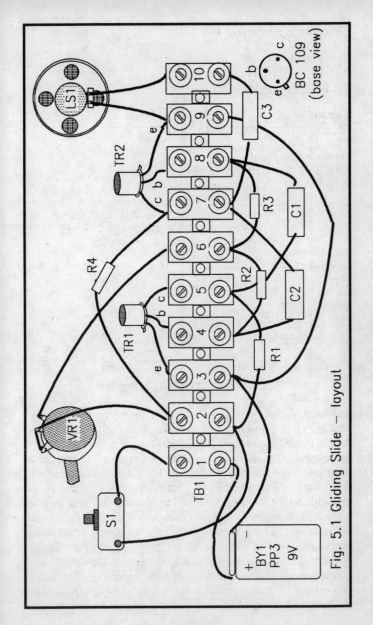

Fig. 5.1 Gliding Slide — layout

23

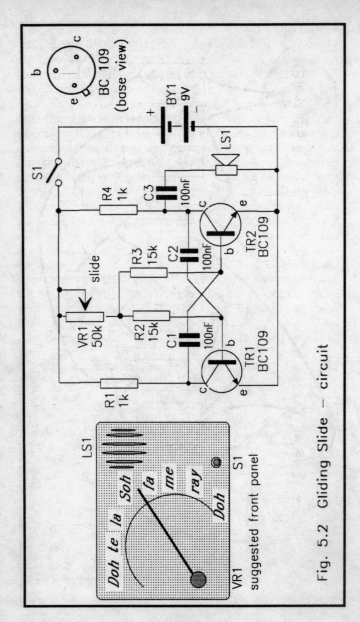

Fig. 5.2 Gliding Slide — circuit

24

Layout (Fig.5.1)

This project needs a 10-way terminal block to reduce over-crowding. Again, it is advisable to use sleeving over the resistor and capacitor leads to avoid short-circuits. The miniature loudspeaker and variable resistor can be mounted on a small plastic project box or on a plywood panel suitably calibrated (see Figure 5.2). A short control arm should be attached either to the VR1 spindle or glued to a control knob to facilitate movement. You can check the pitch against another musical instrument, such as a piano or keyboard, although you may need to borrow the ear of a musical friend. The pitch range can easily be varied by changing C1 and/or C2 values; increase to obtain lower notes, and decrease for higher notes. Similarly, VR1 can be replaced by a higher value to increase the lower end of the scale.

Circuit (Fig.5.2)

The output is taken from the collector of TR2, but could equally be taken from TR1 collector. The coupling capacitor C3 feeds a 64-ohm miniature loudspeaker. If more output is needed, an amplifier input lead could replace the two connections (TB9 and TB10) that go to the speaker.

Components for Project 5

Resistors
R1, R4   1k (2 off)
R2, R3   15k (2 off)

Potentiometer
VR1   50k Lin (see text)

Capacitors
C1 to C3   100nF (3 off)

Semiconductors
TR1, TR2   BC109 (2 off)

Loudspeaker
LS1   64 ohms

Switch
S1   push to make, non-locking

Terminal Block
TB1   10-way

Miscellaneous
9V battery PP3 and clip wire links.

Project 6 – Stylus Organ

A simple electronic organ that plays one note at a time (mono-phonic) is perhaps the next logical step from the last project. In the gliding slide, all the notes were obtained from the 50k variable resistor. However, in this project you will need a number of resistors, one per note, with values that add up to about 50k, if you want the same range. Preset variable resistors are easier to tune than fixed resistors, but may not be practical if soldering is a problem. The measured values of R5 – R16, the octave keyboard, have been listed as a guide.

Layout (Fig.6.1)
The layout is almost identical to the previous project, but the VR1 connection to TB1.2 is broken and two leads are taken off, one to the stylus and the other to the highest note of the key-board, TB2.1.

Keyboard (Fig.6.2)
The simple keyboard shown uses a 12-way terminal block (TB2) but this can be extended if necessary to include more than one octave. Each terminal block connection is screwed to a resistor and a contact key. However, the highest note of the keyboard is tuned in by VR1 and so has no individual resistor in the chain (R5 – R16). In this series chain it is necessary to start at the top note and tune the lower notes in succession as an out of tune note will affect all notes below it. This effect would be eliminated by using a parallel arrangement of resistors, i.e. one end of all resistors would be connected to VR1, the free

26

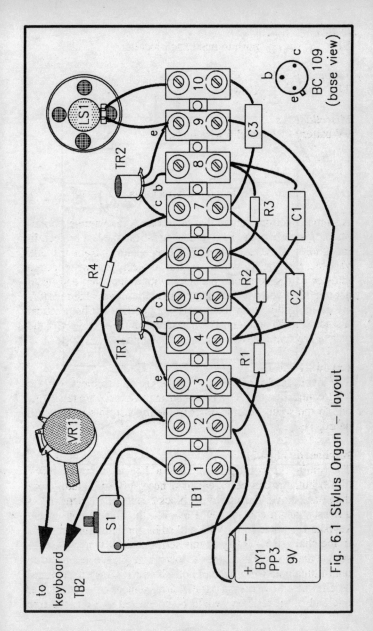

Fig. 6.1 Stylus Organ — layout

27

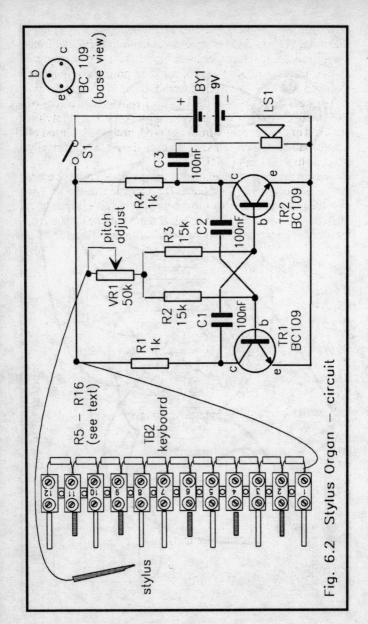

Fig. 6.2 Stylus Organ — circuit

28

ends connected to the keys. This might be a problem without soldering, but you could connect a common link through from the 9V rail using another terminal block. If a parallel arrangement is used the resistor values would be progressively larger (between 1–50k) as the notes descend.

The keys can be short, thick copper rods or flat pieces of aluminium to simulate conventional organ keys. For the stylus, use a rod of thick copper wire, a test prod, or the metal insert of a used ball-point pen. This, of course, should be electrically attached to a lead from VR1.

The circuit is almost identical to the previous project except for the addition of the keyboard. The variable resistor VR1 is now the pitch adjust resistor to set the highest note; it can be a low-value preset resistor if desired. If more volume is required, the speaker connections may be wired to an amplifier.

Components for Project 6

Resistors

R1, R4	1k (2 off)
R2, R3	15k (2 off)
R5	400
R6	1.2k
R7	1.6k
R8	2.7k
R9	3.3k
R10	4.2k
R11	4.5k	measured values
R12	4.9k
R13	6.8k
R14	7.2k
R15	7.8k
R16	8.3k

Potentiometer

VR1	50k Lin (see text)

Capacitors

C1 to C3	100nF (3 off)

Semiconductors
TR1, TR2   BC109 (2 off)

Loudspeaker
LS1   64 ohms

Switch
S1   S.P.S.T. (on/off)

Terminal Block
TB1   10-way
TB2   12-way (see text)

Miscellaneous
9V battery PP3 and clip wire links, stylus and key contacts.

Project 7 – Light and Shade Music

This project appears to pluck 'music' out of thin air. As you wave your arms over this circuit you will be able to produce some unusual sounds. The secret is the light-dependent resistor (LDR), a cadmium sulphide photo-conductive cell, which varies its value from a few ohms in bright sunlight to megohms in total darkness. This takes the place of one of the frequency-determining resistors in a basic astable multivibrator. Just shade the LDR and listen to the pitch of the note plunge into the bass register. Alternatively, expose it to the bright lights and the coloratura soprano takes over. And like the gliding slide project you can produce some spooky vibrato sounds by slowly waving your hand over the photo-cell.

Layout (Fig.7.1)
This project needs only slight circuit changes to the gliding slide described in Project 5. The PCC1, ORP12, replaces a fixed resistor and the resistance value of R2 has been changed. Again, it is worth experimenting with the values of capacitors C1 and C2 if you want other sound effects; decrease values for the higher notes, increase values for the lower notes.

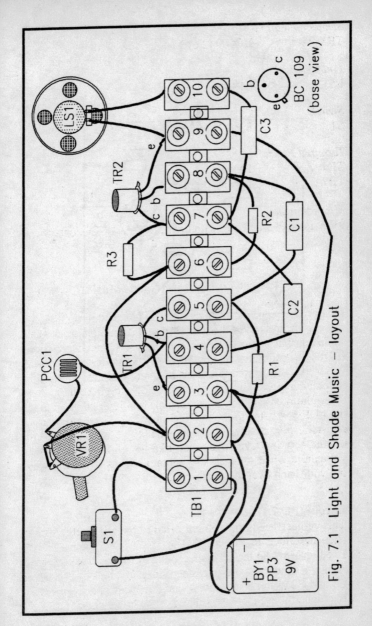

Fig. 7.1 Light and Shade Music – layout

31

The ORP12 resistance will fall
from about 1M in total darkness
to about 6k at 50 lux (a 60W
lamp at 1 metre) and to less
than 100 ohms in sunlight;
the more light, the higher
the pitch of the notes. Use S1
to start and stop the sound.

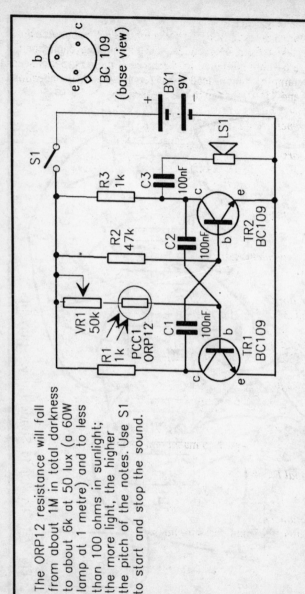

Fig. 7.2 Light and Shade Music — circuit

Circuit (Fig.7.2)

The output is taken from the collector of TR2, but could equally be taken from TR1 collector. The coupling capacitor C3 feeds a 64-ohm miniature loudspeaker. If more output is needed, an amplifier input lead could replace the two connections (TB9 and TB10) that go to the speaker.

Components for Project 7

Resistors
R1, R3   1k (2 off)
R2   47k

Potentiometer
VR1   50k Lin

Light-dependent Resistor
PCC1   ORP12

Capacitors
C1 to C3   100nF (3 off)

Semiconductors
TR1, TR2   BC109 (2 off)

Loudspeaker
LS1   64 ohms

Switch
S1   push to make, non-locking

Terminal Block
TB1   10-way

Miscellaneous
9V battery PP3 and clip wire links.

Project 8 – Warbling Bird

Here's a slight variation on the Hartley oscillator used in the door chime project. This circuit gives a bird sound with a warble rate that can be faster or slower depending on the control setting. A pushbutton control also gives an instantly slower chirp from our warbling bird.

Layout (Fig.8.1)
The main components for this project are accommodated on the 7-way terminal block TB1. A longer terminal block for TB1 would also take the coil L1 and tuning capacitor C2, but it may be easier to use an additional 3-way block TB2 as shown. The coil can be either a tapped transformer winding or the ferrite-cored coil (see Project 3).

Circuit (Fig.8.2)
Resistor R1 and the variable resistor VR1 supply base current for transistor TR1. The values of the tuned circuit L1 and C2 circuit in the collector determine the frequency of oscillations – smaller value of C2 for canaries, larger for chickens! The feedback is from the upper section of coil L1 via C1 to the base of TR1. The warble is produced by the base current charging and discharging the electrolytic capacitor C3 via resistor R2. The warble rate, controlled by VR1, can be further slowed down by pressing S2 to include the electrolytic capacitor C4. If a tapped output transformer is used in place of L1, the loudspeaker can be connected directly across the secondary winding and C5 omitted.

Components for Project 8

Resistors
R1   18k
R2   1k

Potentiometer
VR1   50k Lin

34

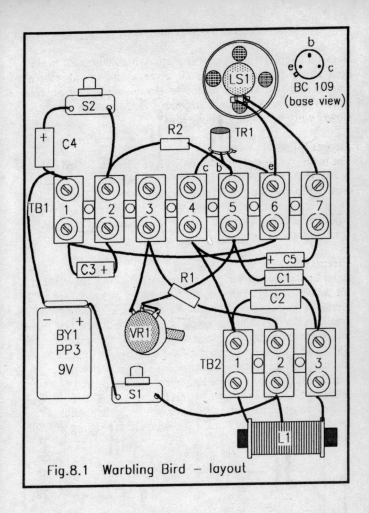

Fig.8.1 Warbling Bird — layout

Capacitors

C1	50nF
C2	100nF
C3	10µF elect. 10V
C4	100µF elect. 10V
C5	1µF elect. 10V

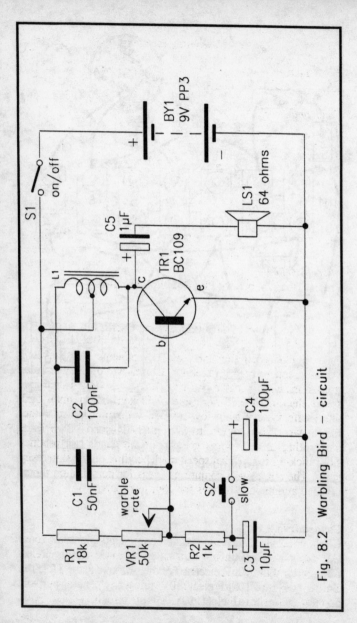

Fig. 8.2 Warbling Bird – circuit

Coil
L1   tapped winding (see text)

Loudspeaker
LS1   64 ohms

Semiconductors
TR1   BC109

Switches
S1   S.P.S.T.
S2   pushbutton non-locking

Terminal Block
TB1   7-way (see text)
TB2   3-way

Miscellaneous
Project Box, 9V battery PP3 and clip wire links.

Project 9 – Sound Effects Oscillator

This simple oscillator has few components but makes a versatile sound effects generator. It uses two directly-coupled transistors, an npn- and a pnp-type. Its basic sound is a variable speed clucking noise, more like a chicken than a small bird. Other effects vary from low-frequency popping noise, rather like a two-stroke engine, to high-pitched sounds. Two leads terminating in bare wires gripped in the hands can produce slow clicking sounds that speed up depending on the skin resistance. The circuit will conjure up ideas for perspiration monitors and audible handshakes for your next party.

Layout (Fig.9.1)
A 9-way terminal block gives the components plenty of room and allows for any changes that may be made to the circuit. Note carefully the connections for the pnp transistor TR2; the emitter goes direct to the +9V rail. Almost any general-purpose pnp transistor should work in this simple circuit.

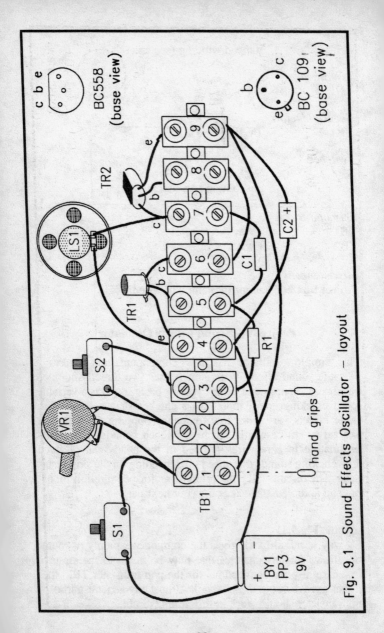

Fig. 9.1 Sound Effects Oscillator — layout

38

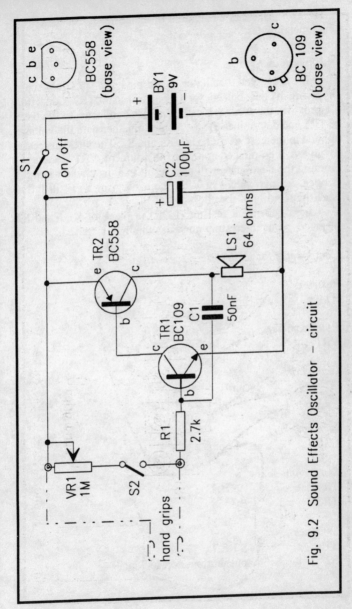

Fig. 9.2 Sound Effects Oscillator – circuit

39

The two grips can be flexible insulated leads connected to small metal plates.

Circuit (Fig.9.2)

The direct-coupled oscillator is formed by TR1 collector supplying the base current for the pnp transistor TR2. Capacitor C1 provides the feedback path from TR2 collector to the base of TR1 and determines the frequency, together with the voltage applied to the base of TR1 via VR1 and S2. The clicks increase to give a high-pitched tone as the value of VR1 decreases. Holding the hand grips will also result in slow clicks when S2 is open. At high values of VR1, the hand grips will still influence the rapidity of the clicks.

A light-dependent resistor (LDR) in place of VR1 and S2 produces some interesting noises as the light is varied.

Components for Project 9

Resistors
R1   2.7k

Potentiometers
VR1   1M Lin

Capacitors
C1   50nF
C2   100µF elect. 10V

Loudspeaker
LS1   64 ohms

Semiconductors
TR1   BC109
TR2   BC558

Switches
S1   S.P.S.T.
S2   pushbutton, non-locking

TB1   9-way (see text)

Miscellaneous
9V battery PP3 and clip wire links.

Project 10 – Audio/Visual Metronome

Keeping to a strict tempo in music is not always easy, and it's even harder to set a given speed. This audio/visual metronome can still keep you on the right track with its flashing LED, whether or not you can hear the beat.

Layout (Fig.10.1)
The layout is almost identical to Project 6, but the frequency-determining capacitors C1 and C2 have been changed to electrolytics and need to be connected the right way round. Correct polarity must also be observed for C3 and the LED D1.

Circuit (Fig.10.2)
The circuit is a very low-frequency astable multivibrator formed by transistors TR1 and TR2. The large cross-coupled capacitors C1 and C2, combined with the fixed resistors R2, R3 and variable resistor VR1 give a frequency range from 1 to 4Hz approximately, i.e. 54–240 beats per minute. These beats are indicated by the flashing LED D1 in the collector of TR2 and give a click in the loudspeaker LS1.

A typical scale is shown and can easily be calibrated by comparing the tempo with another metronome or by counting out the beats per minute against the second-hand of a watch.

Components for Project 10

Resistors
R1   1k
R2, R3   4.7k (2 off)
R4   680

Potentiometer
VR1   50k Lin

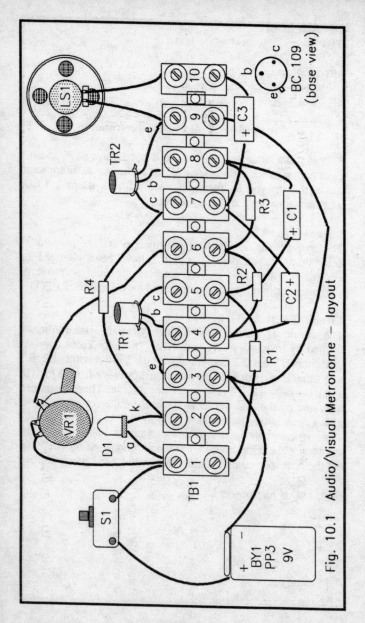

Fig. 10.1 Audio/Visual Metronome – layout

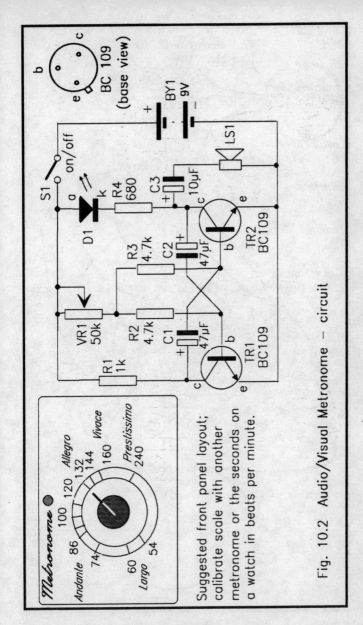

Suggested front panel layout; calibrate scale with another metronome or the seconds on a watch in beats per minute.

Fig. 10.2 Audio/Visual Metronome – circuit

43

Capacitors
C1, C2   47μF elect. 10V (2 off)
C3   10μF elect. 10V

Semiconductors
TR1, TR2   BC109 (2 off)
D1   LED

Loudspeaker
LS1   64 ohms

Switch
S1   S.P.S.T. (on/off)

Terminal Block
TB1   10-way

Miscellaneous
Project Box, 9V battery PP3 and clip wire links.

Chapter 3

ENTERTAINMENT

This chapter includes a number of board and quiz games, some old, some new, with a couple of useful accessories thrown in to see fair play.

Project 11 – Mine Detector Game

Draw a map, locate a few magnets behind it and your party could go with a swing as the contestants endeavour to locate these 'magnetic mines' with a minesweeper circuit. This small unit contains only a handful of components so why not have two minesweepers and make a contest of it. The sensors are magnetic reed switches that bring on a tri-colour LED to indicate the direction of the magnetic mines. These magnetic sensors can be used with magnets on board games or larger maps to locate hidden treasure or to solve quiz clues.

Layout (Fig.11.1)
The layout is very simple and can be assembled on two small terminal blocks, a 4-way (TB1) and a 3-way (TB2). The reed switches RS1 and RS2 must be mounted close to the base of the unit so that they can sense the magnets hidden below the map. The terminal blocks could be screwed to a small piece of ply-wood representing the shape of a boat, or affixed to the base of a small plastic project box. The tri-colour LED D1 and the push switch S1 could be mounted on the lid.

The Map
The map shown suggests a possible layout of an island with mines hidden offshore below the surface. To make minesweep-ing a little more difficult, the detector circuit is only activated when S1 is pressed. A player may only be allowed to press S1 when the minesweeper is stationary and is given an agreed number of attempts to locate a mine. A 'detonate' or direct hit is signalled by an orange glow on D1 (both RS1 and RS2 reed

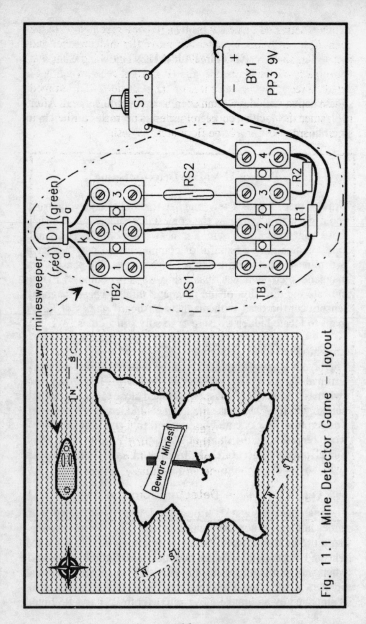

Fig. 11.1 Mine Detector Game – layout

switches activated), a near miss by a red or a green glow. In the event of a near miss, a player can move the minesweeper and press S1 again to try for a direct hit. A green glow indicates that the mine is on the starboard side (RS2 right reed switch activated); a red glow indicates it is on the port side (RS1 left reed switch activated). Players can score according to success. After the game, the mines can be relocated. The map can be on a small board or cover a large floor area, as desired.

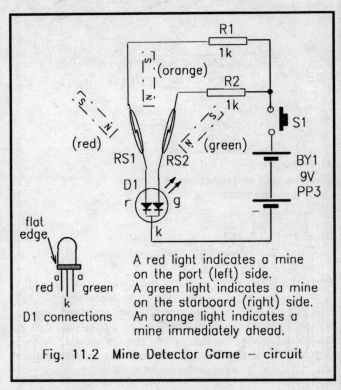

Fig. 11.2 Mine Detector Game — circuit

Circuit (Fig.11.2)

Resistors R1 and R2 are the current-limiters for the red and green diodes of LED D1. Red is indicated when S1 is pressed and RS1 is activated by a magnetic field. Green is indicated when S1 is pressed and RS2 is activated by a magnetic field.

Orange is indicated when S1 is pressed and both RS1 and RS2 are activated magnetically.

Components for Project 11

Resistors
R1, R2   1k (2 off)

Semiconductors
D1   tri-colour LED

Switches
S1   pushbutton, non-locking
RS1, RS2   magnetic reed switches (2 off)

Terminal Block
TB1   4-way
TB2   3-way

Miscellaneous
Plywood base or project box, 9V battery PP3 and clip wire links, map, magnets.

Project 12 – Pinboard Game

Pinboards are usually ball games, but it is easier in this game to flick or slide coins at the pins unless you have a supply of ball-bearings and are good at woodwork. Briefly, the board contains a row of pins which, when contacted by a coin, may switch a tri-colour LED to glow red or green, or even orange. The object is to switch the flip-flop over as many times as possible with say, ten coins. An extra bonus could be given for an orange.

Layout (Fig.12.1)
The main circuit layout is assembled on an 11-way block TB1. Note the pin connections for D1, a tri-colour LED. Three flexible leads are taken off TB1.1, TB1.2 and TB1.6 to the terminal block TB2 that engages the pins in the board (see Fig.12.2).

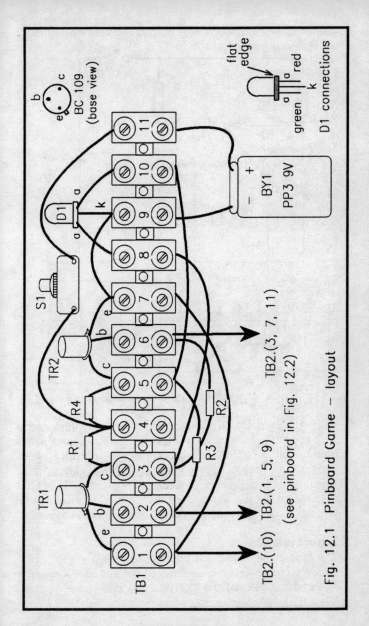

b
•
e • • c
BC 109
(base view)

flat
edge
a   red
green a
k
D1 connections

11
10
+ BY1
− PP3 9V

a
D1
k

a
S1

e
b TR2
c

TB2.(3, 7, 11)

R4
R1

R2
R3

TB2.(1, 5, 9)
(see pinboard in Fig. 12.2)

c
TR1
b
e

TB2.(10)

TB2.(10)

TB1

1 2 3 4 5 6 7 8 9

Fig. 12.1   Pinboard Game − layout

49

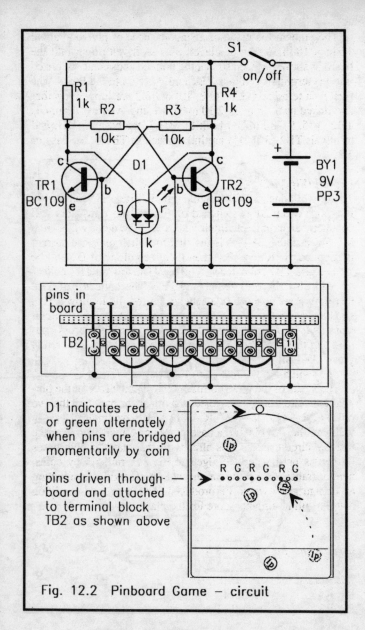

D1 indicates red or green alternately when pins are bridged momentarily by coin

pins driven through board and attached to terminal block TB2 as shown above

Fig. 12.2   Pinboard Game – circuit

The pinboard is made of a smooth piece of plywood about 12-in × 18-in. A row of eleven pins is driven down into the board as shown, spaced so that the pointed ends can be screwed into the terminals of block TB2 end-ways on to the board. The five even terminals (2, 4, 6, 8, 10) of TB2 are looped together and linked back from TB2.10 to TB1.1, the –ve rail. Terminals TB2 (1, 5, 9) are linked back to TB1.2, the base of TR1, and terminals TB2 (3, 7, 11) are linked back to TB1.6, the base of TR2.

Circuit (Fig.12.2)

The circuit consists of a bistable circuit, often referred to as a flip-flop. When S1 is switched on, one of the transistors will conduct, depending on circuit values, and the other will switch off. For instance, if TR1 is the first to switch on (base current is supplied via R4 and R3) then the green diode of D1 will be off because TR1 collector will be low. The low on TR1 collector will also serve to switch off TR2. The collector of TR2 therefore goes positive (via R4) so the red diode glows. This situation persists until TR1 is switched off by a short-circuit from its base to the –ve rail. When this occurs, the cross-coupled resistors switch on TR2 and the diode switches from red to green (TR1 off).

The switching is achieved as follows.

The heads of the pins protruding through the face of the pinboard are alternately connected to a transistor base and the –ve rail, i.e. R – G – R – G – R – G. A coin bridging or briefly touching the –ve pin and a base pin (R or G) will flip over the bistable circuit unless it is already in that state. If both bases have pins permanently bridged to the –ve rail pin by coins, neither transistor will be on and with both anodes conducting an orange glow would be produced. As stated, this condition could result in a bonus score for the player.

Components for Project 12

Resistors

R1, R4   1k (2 off)
R2, R3   10k (2 off)

51

Semiconductors
TR1, TR2   BC109 (2 off)
D1   tri-colour LED

Switches
S1   S.P.S.T.

Terminal Block
TB1   11-way
TB2   11-way

Miscellaneous
Plywood board, panel pins, 9V battery PP3 and clip wire links.

Project 13 – Green-Eyed Cat Game

This game is an electronic update of the old game of threading
a ring around a loop of wire to test your steadiness of hand. In
this version, instead of the sound of a bell or a buzzer if you
make contact, the green, shining eyes of a cat will go out.

Layout (Fig.13.1)
Two terminal blocks are necessary for this project; TB1 to connect the main circuit components and TB2 to support the cat-
shaped loop and the two light-emitting diode 'eyes' D1 and D2.
The cat shape can be made from a loop of thick copper wire –
a wire coat hanger is a suitable source. The two green LEDs
could be mounted on a similar cat-shaped piece of ply or hardboard affixed inside or behind the wire. It will need to be free-
standing because the wire ring has to pass freely around the
wire loop. The loop is supported between TB2.1 and TB2.5. A
short insulating sleeve is fitted at the TB2.5 end so that the wire
ring does not make contact with the wire loop in the start
position. However, at the start, the wire ring must make contact
with the short wire attached to TB2.4 to reset the circuit (TR2
base and emitter short-circuited). Terminal block TB2 can be
mounted on a block of wood to keep the cat-shape stable when
threading the wire ring.

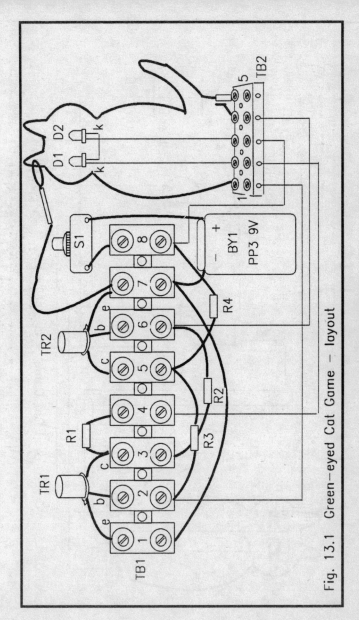

Fig. 13.1 Green—eyed Cat Game — layout

53

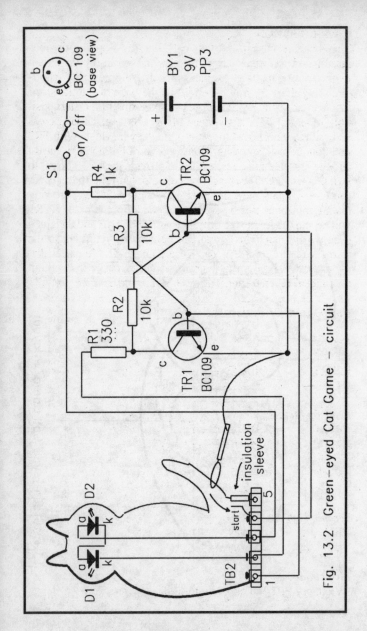

Fig. 13.2 Green-eyed Cat Game — circuit

Circuit (Fig.13.2)

This bistable circuit is often called a flip-flop for obvious reasons. As you can see from the circuit, we can flip the circuit over from one state to the other by momentarily short-circuiting the wire ring (−ve rail) to the base of the transistor that is conducting. For instance, with the ring at the start position, transistor TR2 is switched off by the short-circuit across its base-emitter (TB2.4 to −ve rail via the wire ring). With TR2 non-conducting, the voltage on the +ve rail is applied via R4 and the cross-coupled resistor R3 to provide the base current to switch on TR1. The resulting collector current through R1 causes the green eyes, D1 and D2, to glow. If the wire ring makes contact as it is passed around the loop, the base of TR1 will be shorted to the −ve rail, TR1 will switch off and the green eyes will go out. The circuit can be reset by returning to the start (i.e. short-circuiting TR2 base-emitter). If you prefer that the cat's eyes light up to indicate a contact, rather than go out on contact, reverse connections to TB2.1 and TB2.4.

Components for Project 13

Resistors
R1   330
R2, R3   10k (2 off)
R4   1k

Semiconductors
TR1, TR2   BC109 (2 off)
D1, D2   green LEDs (2 off)

Switch
S1   S.P.S.T.

Terminal Blocks
TB1   8-way
TB2   5-way

Miscellaneous
9V battery PP3 and clip, length of thick wire.

Project 14 – Yes/No? Quiz Game

Quiz games are immensely popular on TV and at social functions. This project allows you to confirm the correct answer to a 'yes/no' question that has been asked. Up to ten questions can be set up, but more could be arranged if desired. A tri-colour LED gives a green light for a 'yes' answer, and a red light for a 'no'. The screw connections on a 10-way terminal strip are connected to the bases of two transistors wired as a flip-flop circuit. A pointer touched on to one of these screws flips over the appropriate transistor and LED colour according to the correct answer.

Layout (Fig.14.1)
This project gets a little cluttered on the main terminal block TB1, so it is better to use sleeved components. The question panel is connected by two wire links from TB1.2 ('yes' busbar) and TB1.6 ('no' busbar). These are looped by a series of short links to all the terminals of TB2 according to whether they require a 'yes' or 'no' answer. After a while, or when a fresh set of answers is used, it is advisable to change the yes/no sequence to prevent it being memorised. The questions can be printed on different pages and clipped to the question panel. Alternatively, TB2 could merely be numbered 1 to 10 and the corresponding questions read out from separate numbered lists.

Circuit (Fig.14.2)
The circuit is a simple RS (set–reset) flip-flop. Depending on the circuit tolerances, at switch-on one of the transistors will conduct. If TR1 conducts initially, it will be held on by a voltage from the +ve rail applied to its base via R4 and R3. The low collector voltage now on TR1, via R2, will hold off TR2 base. The LED D1 will glow red because of the voltage on its anode supplied via R4. Alternatively, if TR2 conducted initially, then TR1 would be non-conducting and D1 would glow green via R1. Changeover is effected by shorting the appropriate transistor base to 0V. The momentary short-circuit on the base-emitter junction causes the transistor to switch off and the other transistor switches on until a short-circuit is applied to its base. This means that by tapping the pointer on to the wired-up

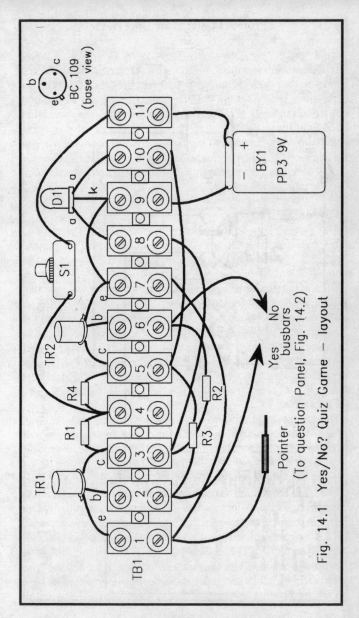

Fig. 14.1 Yes/No? Quiz Game – layout

57

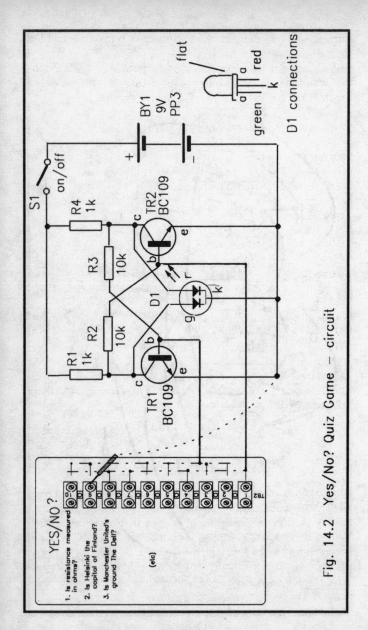

Fig. 14.2 Yes/No? Quiz Game – circuit

58

terminals of TB2 the transistors flip over appropriately and D1 indicates red or green to order.

Switch S1 can be operated after the pointer is making contact or left on, as desired. In the latter case, D1 will be either green or red before indicating the correct answer.

Components for Project 14

Resistors
R1, R4   1k (2 off)
R2, R3   10k (2 off)

Semiconductors
TR1, TR2   BC109 (2 off)
D1   tri-colour LED

Switch
S1   S.P.S.T. or push-to-make, non-locking

Terminal Blocks
TB1   11-way
TB2   10-way

Miscellaneous
Question panel, 9V battery PP3 and clip, conductive pointer and wire links.

Project 15 – Memory Capacity Game

Improve your memory capacity with this simple project, a bank of electrolytic capacitors, charged at the start of the game by a battery. A suggested method of play is that opposing contestants discharge one capacitor in turn to score points. A red or green light flashes momentarily when a charged capacitor is discharged. The problem is remembering which capacitors have already been discharged – no charge, no light, so no point scored! The problem is that charged and discharged capacitors look alike. There are ten capacitors, so ten states to remember,

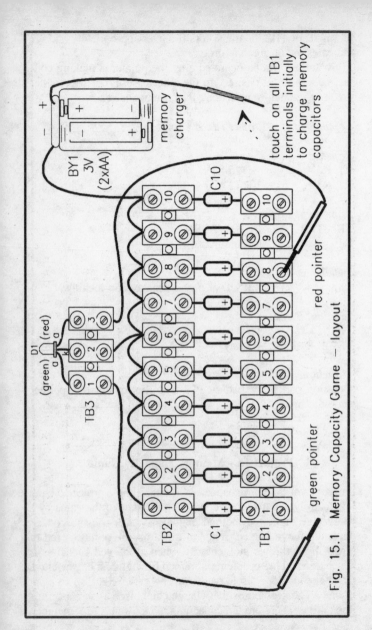

Fig. 15.1 Memory Capacity Game – layout

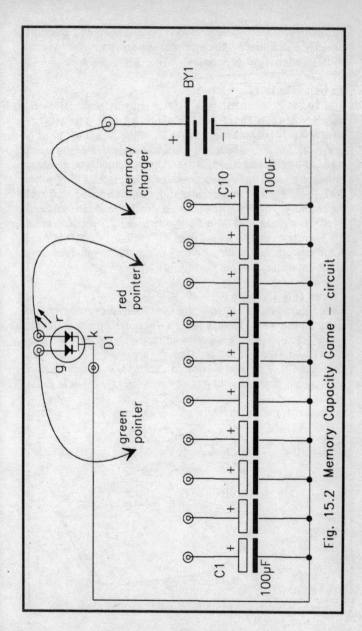

Fig. 15.2 Memory Capacity Game – circuit

61

but the number could be extended by adding more capacitors. So, give a deft touch with your pointers and hope for that flash of inspiration – red or green!

Layout (Fig.15.1)

The layout diagram consists of two ten-way terminal blocks linked by ten capacitors, and a third block for D1. The only reason for TB2 is that the negative sides of the capacitors must be commoned to D1 cathode. Here's where a soldering iron would come in useful; you could also randomly group the positive terminals by using brass paper fasteners in place of the in-line TB2. As suggested, more capacitors could be added to stretch the memory. Three plastic-insulated flexible leads are required; a red and a green lead from TB3 with metallic pointers to touch the +ve contacts, and a lead from the memory charger BY1 (2 AA-type cells in a battery holder) to provide the initial charge to the capacitors.

Circuit (Fig.15.2)

The capacitors are charged by running the memory charger lead along all the +ve terminals in turn. By touching either the red or the green pointer on a +ve terminal the charge in the capacitor will flow through D1 and flash the appropriate colour diode momentarily. This will discharge the capacitor so no further indication is possible until it is charged ready for the next game.

Components for Project 15

Capacitors
C1 to C10   100µF elect. 10V (10 off)

Semiconductors
D1   tri-colour LED

Terminal Blocks
TB1   10-way
TB2   10-way
TB3   3-way

Miscellaneous
BY1 2 x AA-type cells in holder and clip, wire leads.

Project 16 – Electronic Heads/Tails Spinner

The flip-flop circuit is an ideal candidate for devising a heads/tail unit. Drive it from the multivibrator of Project 4 for instance and it is truly electronic. However, to keep the project simple and to introduce another sensing device, a magnetic spinner is employed.

Layout (Fig.16.1)

If you have made up Projects 12 or 14 then you will recognise this layout on 11-way block TB1. It is identical except that the transistor bases are each connected to one end of a reed switch (RS1, RS2). The other ends are returned to the –ve rail (TB1.1). The reed switches can be affixed to a plywood panel suitably spaced between or underneath a spinner arm to which a small magnet is attached. Before making a permanent fixing, ensure that the field of the rotating magnet will activate the reed switches. You can judge the distance by bringing the magnet close to a reed switch – you will hear a faint click as it closes.

Circuit (Fig.16.2)

The bistable circuit formed by transistors TR1 and TR2 and their associated components has already been described in Project 12. Again, the tri-colour LED D1 has been brought into play, this time to represent heads or tails as it glows green or red. Remember that when S1 is switched on, D1 will be either red or green depending on the position of the spinner, or may favour one colour because of the circuit values. However, after a spin, the colour will depend on the last reed switch to close. For some games it may be useful to have a third choice. If the two reed switches are sited near enough to the magnet, both may be activated to give an orange glow – equivalent to a coin landing on its edge, but much more likely!

Components for Project 16

Resistors

R1, R4	1k (2 off)
R2, R3	10k (2 off)

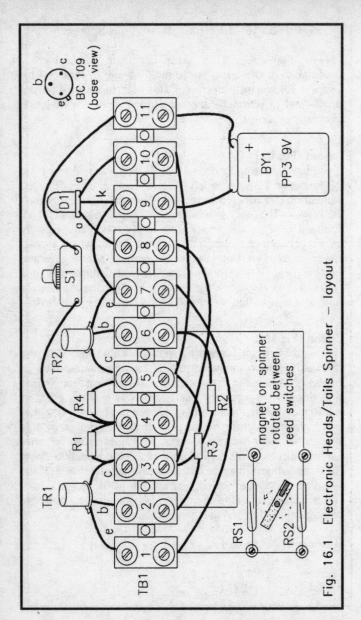

Fig. 16.1 Electronic Heads/Tails Spinner – layout

64

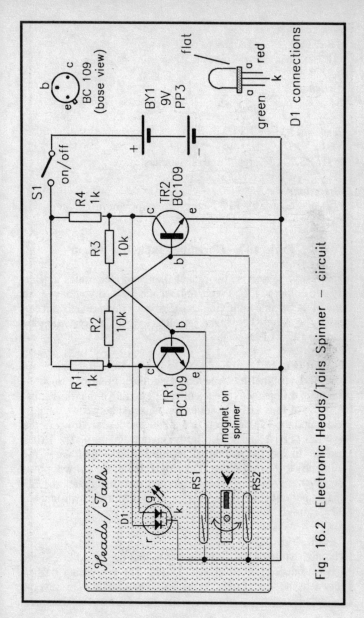

Fig. 16.2 Electronic Heads/Tails Spinner – circuit

65

Semiconductors
TR1, TR2   BC109 (2 off)
D1   tri-colour LED

Switches
S1   S.P.S.T.

Terminal Blocks
TB1   11-way
RS1, RS2   reed 'make' switches

Miscellaneous
Plywood board, 9V PP3 battery and clip wire links.

Project 17 – Christmas Table Decoration

The festive season is always a challenge to electronics ingenuity and coloured LEDs seem to be made for it. If you have tried one of the astable multivibrators (Project 4 onwards) then it can easily be adapted to make an attractive table decoration by adding a few LEDs.

Layout (Fig.17.1)
The TB1 terminal block layout is similar to that of Project 4, the main difference is in the collector circuits of the transistors. A string of four LEDs in series is connected between each collector and the +ve rail. Note that all the anodes face towards the +ve rail (TB1.1 and TB1.6 in the layout diagram). The LEDs can be linked by individual terminal blocks and wires (or soldered) to form a chain. Only two chains are shown, but a BC109 transistor can easily cope with two paralleled, 4-LED chains per collector if a larger capacity battery, for instance a PP9, is used.

Circuit (Fig.17.2)
The multivibrator circuit is similar to that described in Project 4 but produces light instead of sound. The alternating flashes between the two LED chains can be regulated to several seconds by selecting larger capacitors for C1 and C2. There are

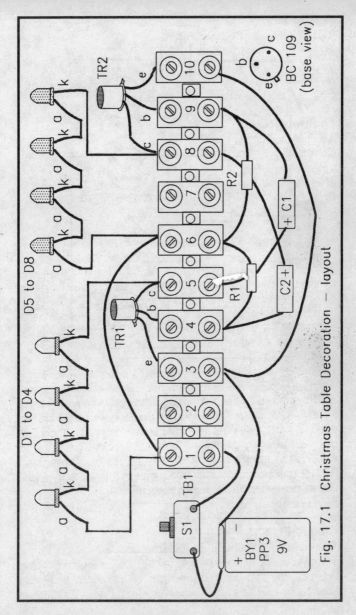

Fig. 17.1 Christmas Table Decoration – layout

67

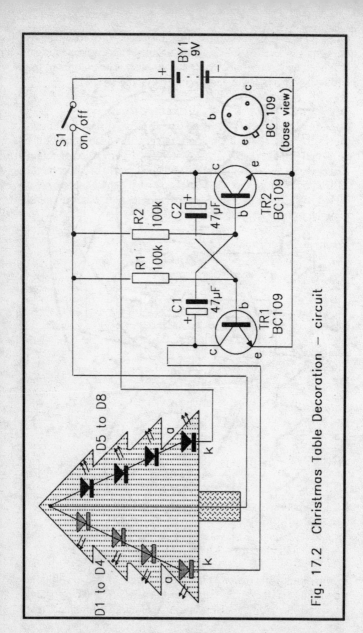

Fig. 17.2 Christmas Table Decoration – circuit

68

other interesting variations. For instance, different values between C1 and C2 will give an unequal mark/space ratio so that one chain stays on longer than the other. The colours of the LEDs can also be arranged to suit individual tastes.

Decorations

The Christmas tree can be made from a piece of flat card or two pieces to give a 3D effect. Alternatively, the decoration could be a bell. If two LED strings were used per collector, eight LEDs could form the shape of one bell, and the other eight LEDs could form another bell shape. If the two shapes were offset, then as the lights flashed from one to the other it would give the impression of a swinging bell.

Components for Project 17

Resistors
R1, R2   100k (2 off)

Capacitors
C1, C2   47µF, 10V (see text) (2 off)

Semiconductors
TR1, TR2   BC109 (2 off)
D1 – D8   LEDs (8 off)

Switch
S1   S.P.S.T.

Terminal Block
TB1   10-way

Miscellaneous
BY1 9V battery and clip, decorating material.

Project 18 – Electronic Cricket Game

In this game of cricket you have to bowl plumb on middle stump to get the man out. And there's no need to shout 'Howzat!' because the electronic 'magic eye' will indicate that the batsman has been clean bowled – the result of metallic contact between middle stump and one of the outer stumps. To bowl, you can either roll a ball bearing, or shove a coin along the pitch. The three stumps are short, thick lengths of copper wire mounted at right-angles in two 3-way terminal blocks. These blocks are screwed down, about 18-in apart, on to a plywood (or hardboard) base.

Rules of Play

The rules are flexible, but here are a few suggestions. The original idea was to have two players, but only as bowlers, since the middle stump is the effective one, and this could be covered up by the bat. However, if we bring in the leg-before-wicket rule and draw a crease at both ends, a pencil-size bat could add to the enjoyment. The bat could preferably be of metal to prevent batsmen shielding the wicket, a touch between stumps would have the same effect as the ball.

So how many can play? Two or more players could make up teams, and even a single player could get in some bowling practice.

- Before switching on, decide who is in the green team and who is in the red team.
- Switch on and whichever light comes on, red or green, that colour team is batting first. The player batting goes in at the wicket indicated by the light.
- The bowler must roll the ball (or shove the coin) from the bowling crease at the other wicket. Assume in this case that the red light is on at the batting end, i.e. the red team bat.
- The batsman must always try to hit the ball or he can be out (bbw) bat-before-wicket. If he succeeds he scores a single each time.
- If the bowler bowls a wide (received beyond the width of the crease) this also counts as a single.
- If the green bowler hits the wicket and the red light goes out then the red batsman is declared out, and his total score is noted. The green light will now be on at the other end.
- One of the red team then takes a turn at bowling to one of the green batsmen at the green end. This continues, the green batsman scoring as before, until he is bowled (the green light goes out and the red light comes on).

70

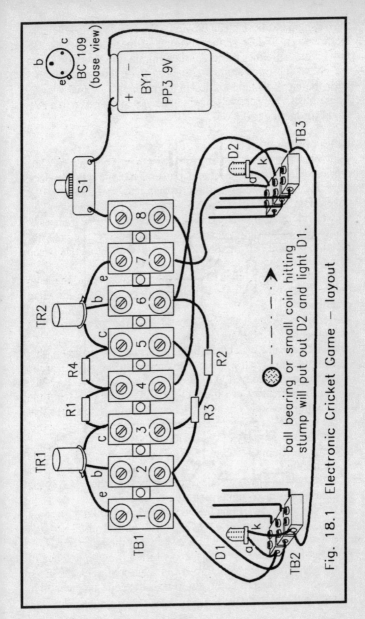

Fig. 18.1 Electronic Cricket Game — layout

ball bearing or small coin hitting stump will put out D2 and light D1.

BC 109 (base view)

71

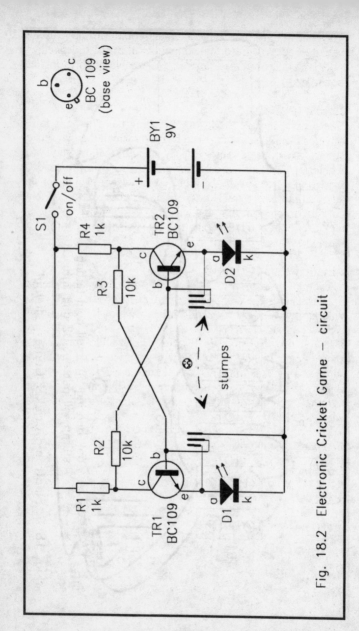

Fig. 18.2 Electronic Cricket Game – circuit

Players from either side bat alternately until all the team has batted, or for an agreed limited number of overs, if desired.

You could, of course, map out a sizeable pitch to include boundaries.

Layout (Fig.18.1)
The general idea of the layout including the stumps is fairly obvious from the drawing. The board on which the two sets of stumps are mounted must be fairly smooth to allow good projection of the 'ball'. If a longer pitch than 18-in is intended, increase the size of the ball and use a wider spacing for the stumps, alternate terminals for instance. Mark out a crease at each end about 2-in from the wickets.

The circuits and interwiring can conveniently be confined to the underside of the pitch.

Circuit (Fig.18.2)
The circuit is the basic RS (set–reset) flip-flop explained before in this chapter. The stumps, aided and abetted by the 'ball', provide emitter-base short-circuit changeover to switch the transistors TR1 and TR2 and consequently the two LEDs, D1 and D2. You may be 'stumped' by the fact that the emitter-base short-circuits include the LEDs between middle and the inside stumps on the diagram. This ploy still has the desired effect and is only done for the convenience of using the two outer terminals to mount the LEDs on the terminal strips behind the wickets.

Components for Project 18

Resistors
R1, R4	1k (2 off)
R2, R3	10k (2 off)

Semiconductors
TR1, TR2	BC109 (2 off)
D1	red LED
D2	green LED

Switch
S1	S.P.S.T.

TB1   8-way
TB2   3-way
TB3   3-way

Miscellaneous
Board for pitch, bat and ball, 9V battery PP3 and clip, and wire links.

Project 19 – Think Tank Game

This is a project to use with a quiz game. It provides a metered total of a player's success in answering questions. Each player has a think tank (a capacitor) that is gradually topped up by correct answers but discharged during thinking time. A fixed-length trigger pulse from the one-shot multivibrator (Project 29) is used to charge the player's capacitor.

Layout (Fig.19.1)

A 12-way terminal block TB1 offers adequate space for the components. The only problem might be the 4-way rotary switch S4; the positive ends of the electrolytic capacitors should preferably be soldered to the switch contacts but could be wire-wrapped. Alternatively, S4 could be replaced by four pushbutton switches or a flying lead with a crocodile clip to select the player's capacitor.

Circuit (Fig.19.2)

An emitter follower TR1, together with meter M1 enables the level of a player's tank to be checked when S3 is pressed. The input resistance of an emitter-follower circuit is high, so reading the meter causes very little drain on the capacitor selected by S4. The chosen capacitors C1 to C4 can receive a fixed charge from the monostable in Project 29, via D1 and R1. When switch S2 (think time discharge) is pressed the capacitor in circuit will discharge slowly through R2.

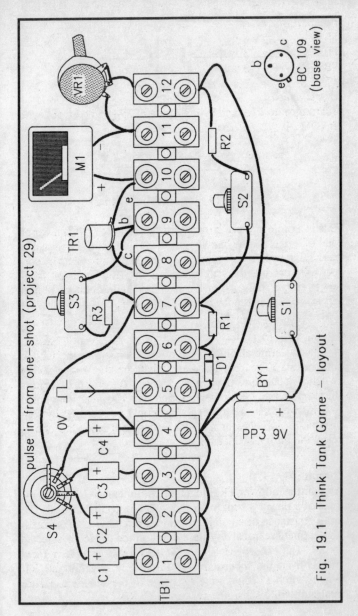

Fig. 19.1 Think Tank Game – layout

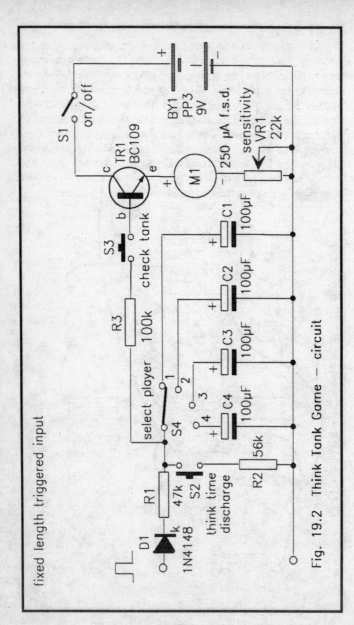

Fig. 19.2 Think Tank Game – circuit

Mode of Play

Up to four players can take part, and are asked questions in rotation. An electrolytic capacitor, C1 – C4, is selected according to which player is answering the quiz controller. When the question has been asked, the controller holds down the pushbutton S2 until the question is answered or the player says 'pass'. This thinking time discharges the player's capacitor, but if he answers correctly he will receive a compensatory fixed charge from the one-shot circuit. At the end of a round it's time to rotate S4 and check tanks (S3) to see who has won. The circuit has many possibilities. I'm sure you can adapt it and formulate your own rules to make an interesting game.

Components for Project 19

Resistors
R1   47k
R2   56k
R3   100k

Potentiometer
VR1   22k Lin

Capacitors
C1 to C4   100µF elect. 10V (4 off)

Meter
M1   250µA

Semiconductors
TR1   BC109
D1   1N4148 signal diode

Switches
S1   S.P.S.T.
S2, S3   pushbutton, non-locking (2 off)
S4   4-way rotary (see text)

Terminal Block
TB1   12-way

Miscellaneous
BY1 9V battery PP3 and clip, and wire links.

Project 20 – Precedence Switch

Many quiz games rely on 'first to press' switches to decide who
is first off the mark with an answer. Precedence switches save
a lot of argument and are the fairest solution for contestants
who are a little backwards in coming forwards. Arm yourself
with two precedence switch pads and it's no longer 'who shouts
wins!'.

Layout (Fig.20.1)
Each switch pad is built around a 6-way terminal block (TB1 or
TB2) and a 3-way block (TB3) serves for the quiz controller's
reset button S3, and battery. The two switch pads, designated
red and green, are both connected to TB3.2 and TB3.3 by twin
insulated cables as shown. A metre of cable will usually be
sufficient to space out the two contestants from the controller.
Three small project boxes can be used for a permanent arrangement.

Circuit (Fig.20.2)
As shown, the two switch pad circuits are identical except that
one LED is red (D1) and the other is green (D2).
    When the quiz controller switches on S3, no current flows
initially because the thyristors Thy1 and Thy2 are not conducting. However, if the contestant with the red switch pad pushes
S1 answer button, a voltage is supplied via R5 and S1 to the
mid-point of potential divider R1, R3 connected to the trigger
gate (g) of Thy1. As a result, current from the battery flows via
R5, through D1 and Thy1 and the red LED glows to indicate
that the red contestant has pressed. Once fired, the thyristor will
remain conducting even when S1 is released, and so LED D1
continues to glow, drawing several milliamps of current
through R5.

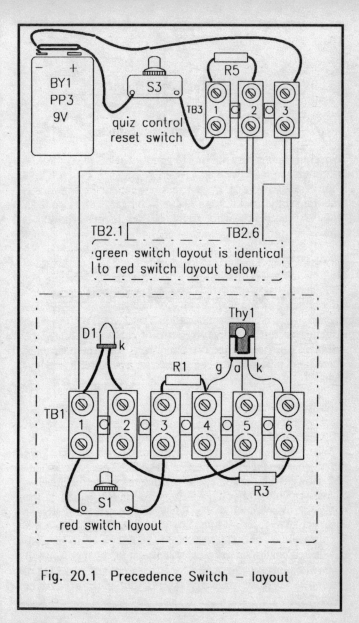

Fig. 20.1 Precedence Switch – layout

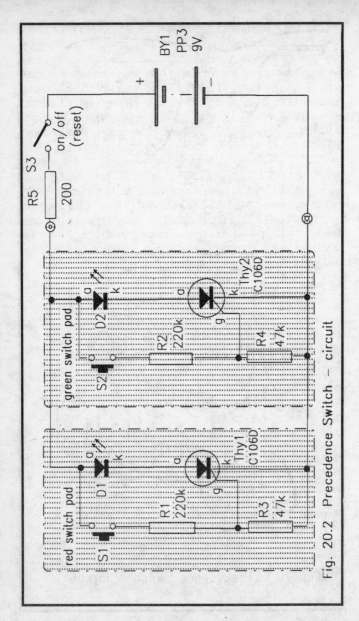

Fig. 20.2 Precedence Switch — circuit

80

If, in the meantime, the green contestant presses his answer button S2, because of the drop in voltage across R5, caused by Thy1 conducting, there will be insufficient current flowing into the gate terminal to fire Thy2 (an over-sensitive thyristor may need a larger value of R1/R2 to ensure it doesn't fire!). Alternatively, if the green contestant presses the S2 button before S1 is pressed, D2 glows and D1 is inhibited.

After each question is answered, the quiz controller must reset S3 – 'off' to switch off the successful contestant's LED, and 'on' to set the circuit for the next question.

As a refinement, the red and green LEDs could be duplicated, in parallel, on the controller's unit. Two extra leads would be needed, one from each LED cathode (TB1.2, TB2.2) to the corresponding LED in the control box. The anodes of the controller's LEDs would be both connected to TB3.2. It may be necessary to reduce the value of R5 to 120 ohms to adjust for the extra current demand.

Components for Project 20

Resistors

R1, R2	220k (2 off)
R3, R4	47k (2 off)
R5	200

Semiconductors

Thy1, Thy2	thyristor C106D (2 off)
D1	red LED
D2	green LED

Switches

S1, S2	pushbutton, non-locking (2 off)
S3	S.P.S.T.

Terminal Blocks

TB1, TB2	6-way (2 off)
TB3	3-way

Miscellaneous

BY1 9V battery PP3 and clip, and insulated twin cables.

Project 21 – Games Timer

Board games can be boring games, as I'm sometimes reminded, when a player takes what seems an age to think about the next move. Limited thinking time is the answer, and a simple games timer offers a practical solution. This circuit measures the time taken for a large capacitor to charge through a variable resistor and switch on a buzzer.

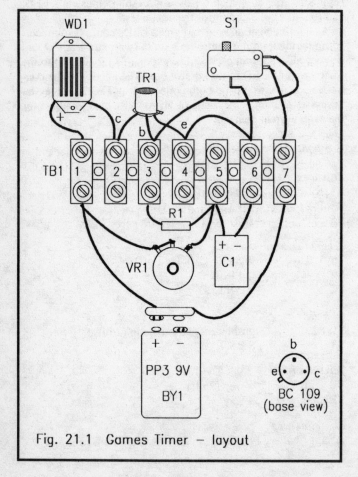

Fig. 21.1 Games Timer – layout

Layout (Fig.21.1)

The components are grouped on a 7-way terminal block TB1 as shown. Ensure that correct polarity of C1, WD1 and the battery connections is observed. The variable resistor VR1 can be calibrated in seconds against a watch. The layout diagram shows the front view of VR1 connections, i.e. as the control is turned clockwise, the resistance is increased to increase the time interval. The three connections to the changeover switch S1 can be wire-wrapped or preferably soldered.

Circuit (Fig.21.2)

The large electrolytic capacitor C1 is charged through the variable resistor VR1 from the +9V rail when the changeover switch S1 is held down. Alternatively, S1 can be a changeover slider switch. When C1 charges sufficiently for the base voltage on TR1 to exceed 0.7V approximately, the transistor switches on and the collector current energises the solid-state buzzer WD1. The CR time constant in seconds will depend on the values of C1 and VR1 setting. The release contact of S1 discharges C1 via R1 ready for the next timing cycle.

If a visual indication of elapsed time is acceptable, WD1 can be replaced with an LED and 470 ohm resistor in series. The correct polarity must be observed for the LED, i.e. anode towards +ve rail.

Components for Project 21

Resistors
R1   2.2k

Potentiometer
VR1   250k Lin

Capacitor
C1   2200µF elect. 10V

Switch
S1   changeover microswitch or slider

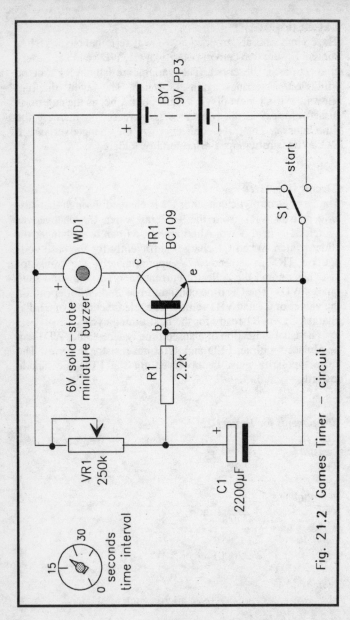

Fig. 21.2 Games Timer – circuit

Semiconductors
TR1   BC109
WD1   6V solid-state miniature buzzer

Terminal Block
TB1   7-way

Miscellaneous
BY1 9V PP3 battery and clip, wire leads.

Chapter 4

SECURITY DEVICES

Alarms, security lights, sensor switches and deterrents are all part of today's crime prevention scene. This chapter offers a number of security projects to help you sleep more peacefully when you pull up the drawbridge at night.

Project 22 – Burglar Alarm ('Break' Contacts)

This burglar alarm project is suitable to protect several points where intruders could gain access. The circuit employs a number of closed contacts in series. These may be magnetic reed switches and microswitches attached to doors, or strands of wire taped across windows. Any break in these contacts will cause an alarm to sound until it is switched off.

Layout (Fig.22.1)
The complete circuit except for the burglar 'break' switches is easily built on the 7-way terminal block TB1. It may be necessary to extend the leads of the thyristor Thy1. If soldering is not possible, remember that single terminal blocks can easily be cut from a multi-way block to deal with such extensions. The thyristor is capable of passing higher current than demanded by the miniature buzzer shown; if desired, you could use a high power buzzer or an electric bell.

Circuit (Fig.22.2)
The series of burglar switches, S2 to S4, or more depending on the points of access, connect the base of TR1 to its emitter circuit and so hold the transistor off. However, if one of the contacts opens, base current is applied to TR1 from the +ve rail via R1 and R2 and the transistor conducts. The voltage in the emitter circuit developed across R4 applies current to the gate to switch on the thyristor Thy1 (sometimes referred to as a silicon-controlled rectifier). Consequently, the alarm WD1 in series with Thy1 is activated by the current flowing between

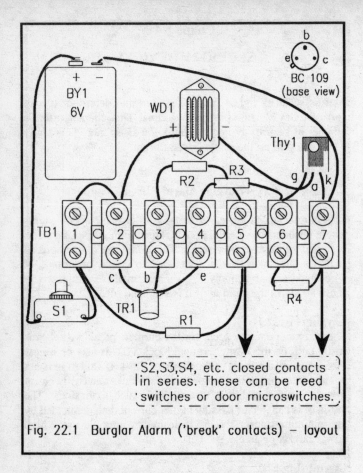

Fig. 22.1 Burglar Alarm ('break' contacts) — layout

anode and cathode. Once the gate is fired, the thyristor exhibits little resistance so has low power loss. It is self-latching until the forward current is removed by the set/reset switch S1.

Components for Project 22

Resistors
R1   47k
R2, R3, R4 1k (3 off)

88

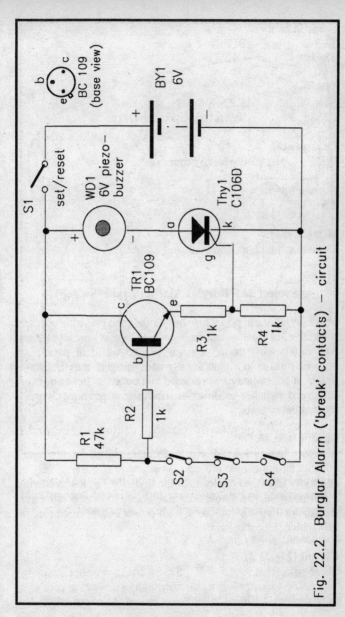

Fig. 22.2 Burglar Alarm ('break' contacts) – circuit

89

Semiconductors
TR1   BC109
Thy1   C106D

Switches
S1   S.P.S.T.
S2, S3, S4   'break' contacts (see text)

Loudspeaker
WD1   6V piezo buzzer

Terminal Block
TB1   7-way

Miscellaneous
6V battery and clip, and insulated cable.

Project 23 – Burglar Alarm ('Make' Switch)

This burglar alarm project is simpler than the previous one, and is suitable for 'make' contact instead of 'break' contact sensors. Any number of 'make' contacts can be wired in parallel as intruder sensors to trigger the thyristor that activates the alarm. Points of access may be protected by contact switches or magnetic reed switches on doors or windows, or pressure switches located under mats.

Layout (Fig.23.1)
A 6-way terminal block easily accommodates the few components in this simple project. As stated previously, it may be necessary to extend the leads of the thyristor Thy1. If soldering is not possible, use single terminal blocks to extend the wires. Again, the thyristor can take a high-power buzzer or an electric bell with a bigger battery.

Circuit (Fig.23.2)
Three paralleled switches S2, S3, S4 are shown, but any number can be used depending on how many points of access need to be covered. When switch S1 is closed the alarm is set. The

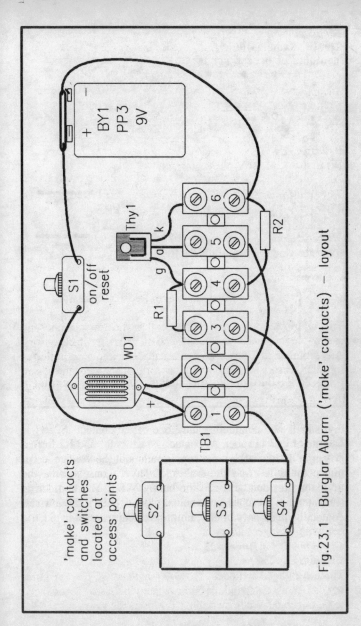

'make' contacts
and switches
located at
access points

Fig.23.1 Burglar Alarm ('make' contacts) – layout

91

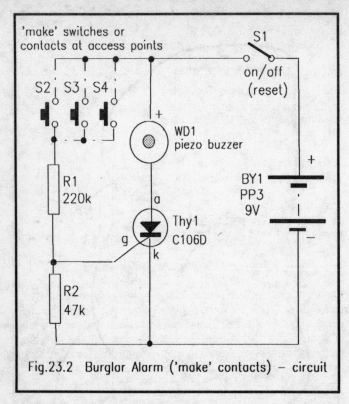

Fig.23.2 Burglar Alarm ('make' contacts) – circuit

thyristor is non-conducting until one of the contacts S2–S4 is operated by an intruder. At contact, resistors R1 and R2 form a potential divider across the supply rails and the voltage at the mid-point is fed into the gate g of Thy1. Consequently, the thyristor fires and activates the buzzer WD1. The thyristor is self-latching; the alarm continues to sound, even if the intruder contact is made only briefly, until the circuit is reset by S1.

Components for Project 23

Resistors
R1   220k
R2   47k

Switches
S1   S.P.S.T.
S2, S3, S4   'make' contacts (see text)

Loudspeaker
WD1   6V piezo buzzer

Terminal Block
TB1   6-way

Semiconductors
Thy1   thyristor C106D

Miscellaneous
9V battery, PP3 or PP9, and clip.

Project 24 – Intruder Deterrent

There are many intruder deterrents in current use: barbed wire, guard dogs, security lights, fake alarms, etc. Here is the ubiquitous multivibrator again, a simple circuit that you can put in your car, or in a prominent place in the entrance to your premises that simply flashes to make a would-be intruder think twice about breaking in.

Layout (Fig.24.1)
A 10-way terminal block takes all components including the two LEDs. If used as a car thief deterrent, the supply can be taken from a cigar lighter adaptor socket, although the circuit only takes a few milliamps. As a deterrent, this project will probably look more perplexing to an intruder as a cluster of components, rather than mounted in a project box.

Circuit (Fig.24.2)
The astable multivibrator needs little explanation as it has been described from Project 4 onwards. Light-emitting diodes D1 and D2 in the collector circuits will flash alternately at a rate determined by the time constants of C1,R3 and C2,R2. Increase these values if a slower flashing rate is required, and vice versa.

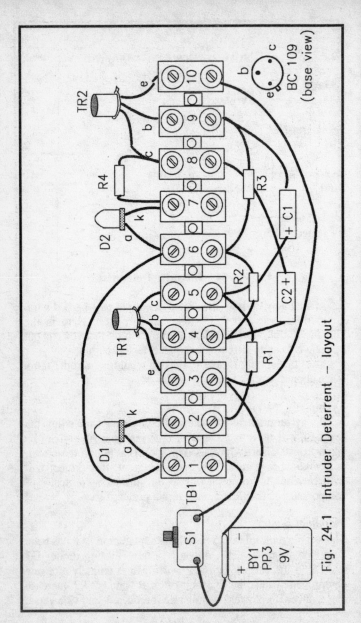

Fig. 24.1 Intruder Deterrent – layout

94

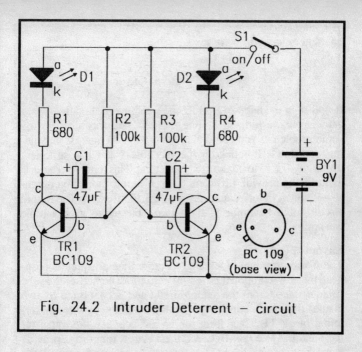

Fig. 24.2   Intruder Deterrent — circuit

Components for Project 24

Resistors
R1, R4   680 (2 off)
R2, R3   100k

Capacitors
C1, C2   47µF elect. 10V (2 off)

Switch
S1   S.P.S.T.

Terminal Block
TB1   10-way

Semiconductors
TR1, TR2   BC109 (2 off)
D1, D2   LEDs (2 off)

9V battery and clip, wire links.

Project 25 – Rain Sensor

If you're in the habit of leaving the sunshine roof open on your car, or your washing on the line, this rain sensor could save you some problems. You could also use it to warn against impending overflows. It relies on the fact that water has sufficient impurities in it to make it conductive. This characteristic is exploited to provide sufficient base current to switch on a transistor, which in turn causes a warning LED to glow. The output circuit could be replaced by a piezo buzzer to give audible warning.

Layout (Fig.25.1)
The 6-way terminal block TB1 is more than adequate to connect the few components for this circuit. The sensor may be some distance from the indoor circuit and is connected by two insulated wires. It consists of parallel bare copper wires on terminal block TB2 that form the circuit between the transistor base and the +ve rail. Between these wires, rain drops provide a conductive path for base current to switch on the transistor. The LED D1 can be replaced by a buzzer if desired.

Circuit (Fig.25.2)
The sensor wires and the variable resistor VR1 act as a potential divider across the supply rails. Under dry conditions, the voltage across VR1 must be less than about 0.7V so that transistor TR1 is not conductive. When the base of TR1 exceeds 0.7V, i.e. when raindrops across the sensing wires cause conduction, then TR1 switches on and collector current flows, bringing on the warning LED, D1. The variable resistor VR1 should be adjusted, with a moist finger across the sensor wires, so that the LED just glows. When the wires dry out, the LED will switch off. Resistor R1 protects TR1 from excessive base current if TB2 contacts are accidentally short-circuited.

As shown, the circuit could also be used to indicate water levels. For instance, two parallel wires could be suspended over a water tank to indicate when it is full.

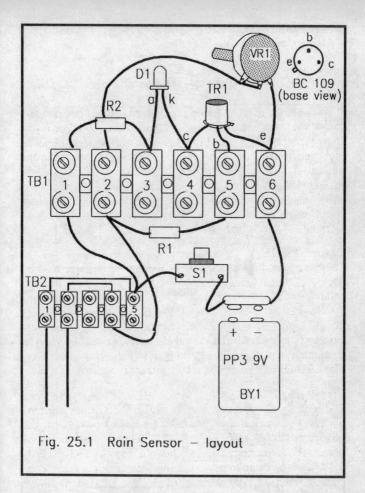

Fig. 25.1 Rain Sensor — layout

Components for Project 25

Resistors

R1	1k
R2	470

Potentiometer

VR1	500k Lin

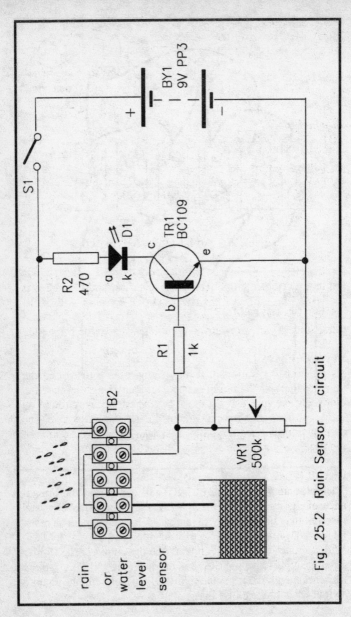

Fig. 25.2 Rain Sensor — circuit

Semiconductors
TR1   BC109
D1   LED

Switch
S1   S.P.S.T.

Terminal Block
TB1   6-way

Miscellaneous
9V battery and clip, and insulated wires.

Project 26 – Sound-Operated Switch

This project is designed to bring on a light when sounds impinge on the microphone. However, if an audible alarm is preferred, the transistor switch triggers a thyristor with sufficient power to operate a buzzer, bell or a relay. The single transistor stage is not very sensitive but it illustrates the principle.

Layout (Fig.26.1)
As previously mentioned, it may be necessary to extend the thyristor leads by soldering or using auxiliary single connecting blocks. Make sure that the leads are the correct way round on Thy1; the diagram shows it from the metallic heatsink side. The current rating of the 6V lamp, LP1, can be 60mA, 100mA or more depending on the capacity of the 6-volt battery.

Circuit (Fig.26.2)
The value and adjustment of VR1 will depend on the impedance of the microphone used. With a high impedance crystal insert, it may be necessary to increase VR1 and connect a resistor of 47k across the insert to limit the base current to TR1. With a sound input, TR1 conducts and the output in the emitter circuit triggers the gate of the thyristor, Thy1. This rapidly switches the thyristor on and lights LP1, which remains on until switch S1 is broken.

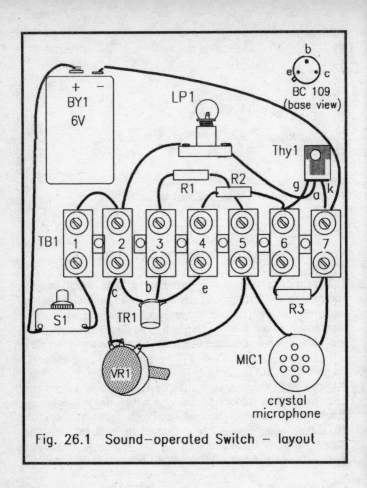

Fig. 26.1   Sound—operated Switch — layout

Components for Project 26

Resistors
R1, R2, R3   1k (3 off)

Potentiometer
VR1   500k Lin (see text)

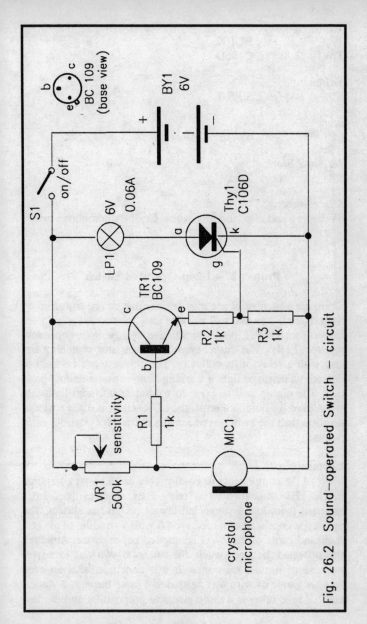

Fig. 26.2 Sound-operated Switch — circuit

Semiconductor
TR1   BC109
Thy1   C106D

Switch
S1   S.P.S.T

Lamp
LP1   6V (see text)

Terminal Block
TB1   7-way

Miscellaneous
6V battery and clip, and link wires. Crystal microphone insert.

Project 27 – Light-Operated Switch

There are a number of security devices that can be triggered by light. Here is one that will activate a switch contact when light falls on an ORP12 photo-conductive cell or light-dependent resistor (LDR). The output controls a transistor switching circuit with a relay in its collector. The contacts can be used to operate an alarm or light a warning lamp in some remote position. The circuit will respond to natural or artificial light and when used for burglar alarms, the LDR sensor is often easier to position than the switch-type sensors needed for possible entry points.

Layout (Fig.27.1)
Most of the components fit comfortably on the 6-way terminal block TB1 as shown. The relay RL1 requires four extra terminal pairs and a suggested layout on TB2 is shown. The prototype consisted of a reed switch with a winding of about a thousand turns of 32 SWG enamelled copper wire. Although this operated the reed switch, the current drawn was excessive because of its low resistance. It was concluded that an even smaller gauge of wire was needed and more turns. A commercial 5V reed relay is a more practical proposition and the lay-

out will depend on the relay in use. However, you need to organise for soldered wire ends to be attached to relays that have short pin connections.

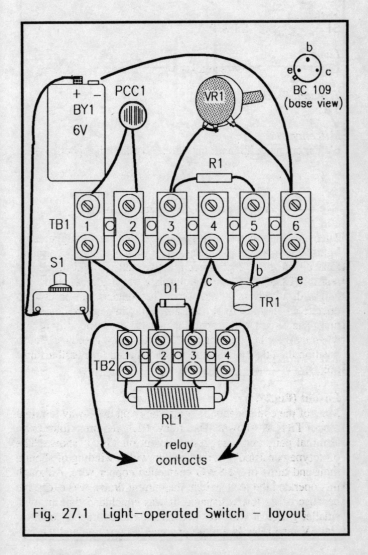

Fig. 27.1 Light–operated Switch – layout

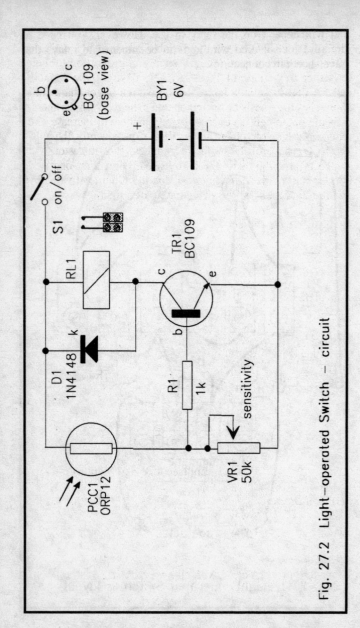

Fig. 27.2 Light-operated Switch – circuit

Circuit (Fig.27.2)

The photo-cell PCC1 and the variable resistor VR1 act as a potential divider to share the 6V supply in proportion to their resistance to the base of TR1 via R1. In daylight, the variable resistor VR1 is initially increased to give it a larger share until it switches the transistor on and operates the relay. In darkness, or if the photo-cell is covered, its resistance will increase and reduce the share of voltage across VR1. Consequently, the voltage to the base of TR1 will be reduced, the transistor will switch off and the relay will be released. For a light-operated burglar alarm, this is the quiescent condition until activated by an intruder's torch, or the switching on of a light.

Components for Project 27

Resistor
R1   1k

Potentiometer
VR1   50k Lin

Semiconductors
TR1   BC109
D1   1N4148
PCC1   ORP12

Switch
S1   S.P.S.T.

Relay
RL1   5V reed relay (see text, e.g. Maplin)

Terminal Blocks
TB1   6-way
TB2   4-way

Miscellaneous
6V battery (4 × AA cells) with clip, wire links.

Project 28 – Automatic Night Light

This project uses a similar circuit to that used by local authorities to bring on the lights on the public highway 'when day is done and shadows fall'. In this case it's nothing so imposing as a street lamp that is automatically operated by our ORP12 photo-conductive cell, but just a 6V 0.06A MES bulb. However, this would be quite adequate for a small night light for a child's bedroom. It would automatically come on at dusk, and go off at dawn or if the room light is left on.

Layout (Fig.28.1)
There is plenty of room on the 6-way terminal block TB1 for the few components. The MES-type bulb is fitted in a batten

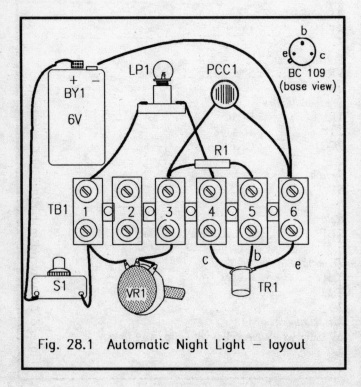

Fig. 28.1 Automatic Night Light – layout

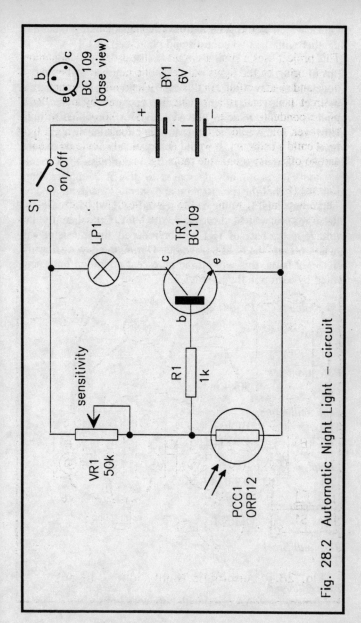

Fig. 28.2 Automatic Night Light — circuit

holder, which would need to be on the outside of a project box together with the two controls and photo-cell PCC1.

Circuit (Fig.28.2)

As explained in Project 27, the light-operated switch, the photo-cell PCC1 and the variable resistor VR1 act as a potential divider to share the 6V supply proportional to their resistance to the base of TR1. In this circuit the two components VR1 and PCC1 are now reversed because we need the circuit to switch on at night. This time, in darkness, the variable resistor VR1 is initially decreased to give it a smaller share until it switches the transistor on and operates the light. In daylight or artificial light the resistance of PCC1 will decrease and more voltage will be dropped across VR1. Consequently, the voltage to the base of TR1 will be reduced, the transistor will switch off and the light will go out. During the day, or if artificial light is on, this will be the quiescent condition until activated by a drop in the light level.

Components for Project 28

Resistor
R1   1k

Potentiometer
VR1   50k Lin

Semiconductors
TR1   BC109
PCC1   ORP12

Lamp
LP1   6V 0.06A MES

Switch
S1   S.P.S.T.

Terminal Block
TB1   6-way

Miscellaneous
6V battery (4 × AA cells) with clip, wire links.

Project 29 – One-Shot Multivibrator

This is a multivibrator with a difference. When triggered it produces one rectangular pulse of a fixed length which can be useful for several applications. For instance, if you, say, want to trigger a light gun for use on a target that is based on Project 27 or give a fixed charge to a capacitor (Project 19), a monostable circuit such as this will do the trick!

Layout (Fig.29.1)

All components are mounted on a 9-way terminal block, but the operation of the project can only be effective if the pulse on the output can be utilised. All projects in this book have practical applications and two have already been suggested. An LED and limiter resistor can be connected to the output (TB1.1 and TB1.5), as shown, to test the circuit.

Circuit (Fig.29.2)

The monostable, a device with one stable output, is formed by transistor amplifiers TR1 and TR2 in a feedback circuit. When the circuit is switched on by S1, transistor TR2 conducts because base current is applied via R2. With TR2 conducting, its collector will be low. If a trigger pulse occurs, i.e. switch S2 is pressed, then base current via R5 switches on TR1. The low on TR1 collector is applied via C1 to the base of TR2 which switches off for an interval depending on the value of the timing components C1, R2. This switch-off time applied to the base of TR2 gives a short positive pulse at the collector, which can be used to light an LED as shown, or used for the other applications mentioned.

Components for Project 29

Resistors

R1, R4	1k (2 off)
R2, R3, R5	10k (3 off)
R6	470 (see text)

Capacitor

C1	10µF elect. 10V (see text)

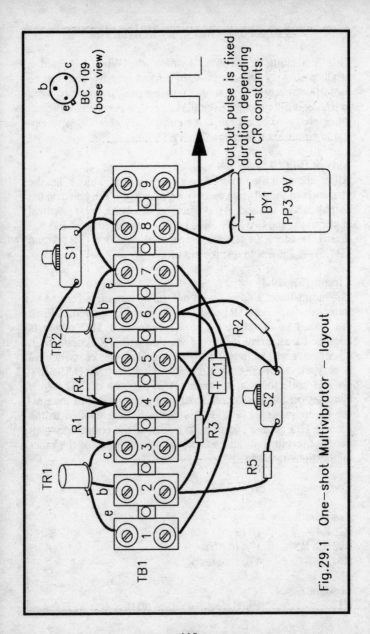

Fig.29.1 One-shot Multivibrator — layout

110

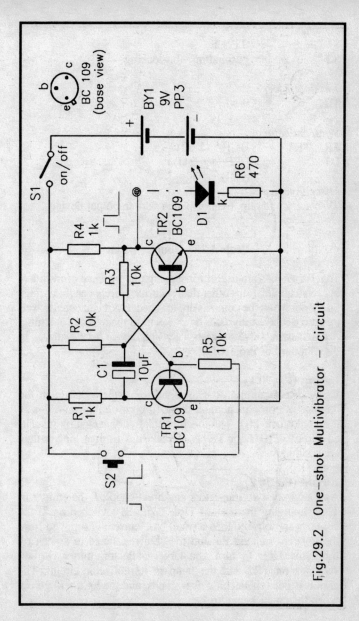

Fig.29.2 One-shot Multivibrator — circuit

111

Switches
S1   S.P.S.T.
S2   pushbutton, non-locking

Terminal Block
TB1   9-way

Semiconductors
TR1, TR2   BC109 (2 off)
D1   LED (see text)

Miscellaneous
9V battery and clip, twin insulated wire to output devices.

Project 30 – Touch Switch

Touch switches are useful for sensing the presence of intruders but have applications other than security. Here's one that brings on a light when the contacts are touched, but it can equally well operate a relay, a thyristor or an alarm to make it self-latching. A touch switch also suggests a sensing device for a game, as in the pinboard of Project 12.

Layout (Fig.30.1)
Using direct coupling between the transistors cuts down the number of components and these fit comfortably on a 7-way terminal block TB1. The touch contacts, connected by insulated wires to TB1.1 and TB1.3, can take any form as long as they are conductive.

Circuit (Fig.30.2)
As stated, the two transistors are direct-coupled, the emitter of TR1 supplying the base of TR2. With S1 switched on, if the contacts are touched then a small base current is supplied from the positive rail via R1 and the skin resistance to switch on transistor TR1. In turn, the larger collector-emitter current, switches on TR2 and the lamp in its collector circuit. The circuit is not self-latching as it stands, and the light will go out when the contacts are broken.

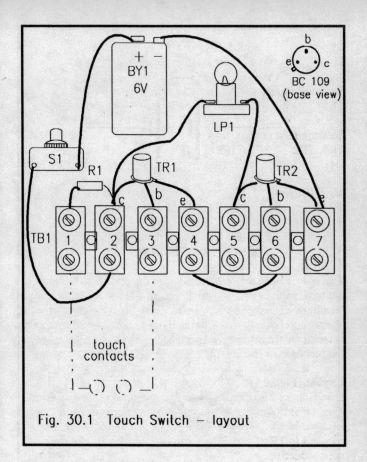

Fig. 30.1 Touch Switch — layout

Components for Project 30

Resistor
R1   100k

Semiconductors
TR1, TR2   BC109 (2 off)

Switch
S1   S.P.S.T.

113

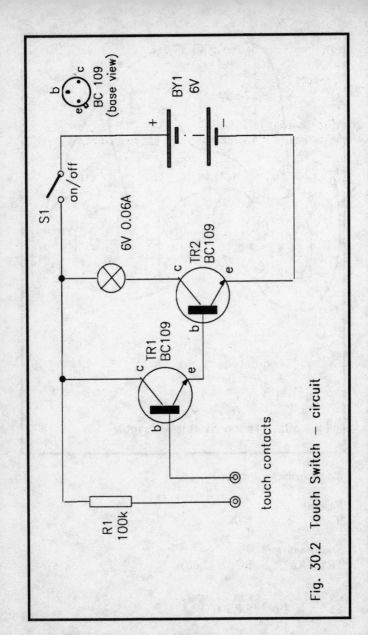

Fig. 30.2 Touch Switch — circuit

114

Lamp
LP1   6V, 0.06A (see text)

Terminal Block
TB1   7-way

Miscellaneous
6V battery (4 × AA cells) and clip, and link wires.

Chapter 5

COMMUNICATION

The early days of wireless were all about communication. There's a reminder of those pioneering days with this project, and notice the improvement when we add a bit of amplification with a modern transistor.

Project 31 – Crystal Set

No! This crystal set is nothing to do with cut-glass ware; in fact it's a modern version of the classic 'cat's whisker' crystal set of the early days of radio. It needs no batteries because it is powered by the radio signal you receive. However, it does need a long, high aerial connected to it, and a good, clean earth connection to a cold water pipe or to a metal rod in the ground. If you live near a local radio station broadcasting on the medium wave you should have no trouble in picking it up on your crystal earpiece – the difficulty might be in hearing any other stations. The prototype took about five minutes to hook up, and in Felixstowe, Suffolk, I could tune in the local radio station and French and Dutch stations – not very loud, but intelligible.

Layout and Circuit (Fig.31.1)
The 6-way terminal block, TB1, is more than able to accommodate the five components needed for this project. The ferrite rod and coil can be obtained commercially, but it is cheaper to wind 50 turns of insulated wire, closely spaced on a six-inch length of three-eighth-inch ferrite rod and bring the ends out to the terminal block as shown.

The circuit is surprisingly simple. This is why you need a good outdoor aerial. The radio waves received by the aerial set up alternating currents of different frequencies which can be selected by the tuned circuit comprising the coil L1 and the variable capacitor VC1. The sensitive germanium point-contact diode, D1, passes only the positive-going swings of the high-frequency signal and so rectifies it into a varying d.c. signal.

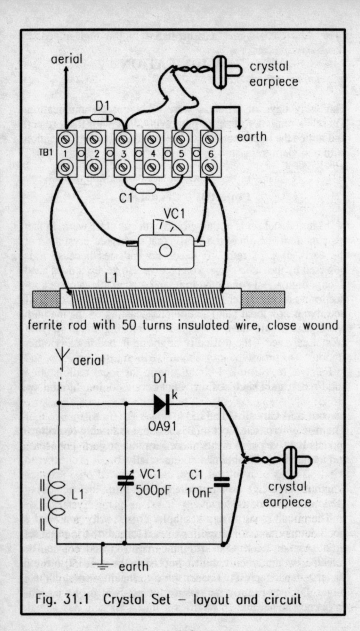

ferrite rod with 50 turns insulated wire, close wound

Fig. 31.1 Crystal Set — layout and circuit

118

This 'detected' signal can be heard in the high-impedance crystal earpiece.

Components for Project 31

Capacitors
VC1   500pF variable tuning capacitor
C1   10nF plastic foil

Semiconductor
D1   OA91 point-contact germanium diode

Terminal Block
TB1   6-way

Earpiece
Crystal high impedance (Maplin)
Can be wired direct or with 3.5mm jack plug and socket.

Miscellaneous
Insulated wire for aerial and earth connections.

Project 32 – Transistor Radio

If the crystal set project was not powerful enough, then you could give the audio output a boost with a one-stage transistor amplifier. A battery is required to power the transistor and there is sufficient volume for a small speaker. However, you will still probably need a high aerial and a good, clean earth connection to get a strong signal.

Layout (Fig.32.1)
The 'front end' of the receiver is the same as the crystal set, but the terminal block, TB1, has been changed for a 9-way to include the transistor amplifier stage TR1 and the loudspeaker LS1. As for the crystal set, the ferrite rod and coil can be obtained commercially, but it is cheaper to wind 50 turns of insulated wire, closely spaced on a six-inch length of three-eighth-inch ferrite rod and bring the ends out to the terminal block as shown.

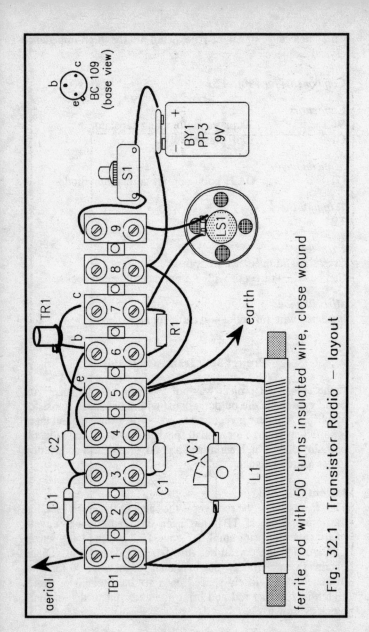

Fig. 32.1 Transistor Radio – layout

ferrite rod with 50 turns insulated wire, close wound

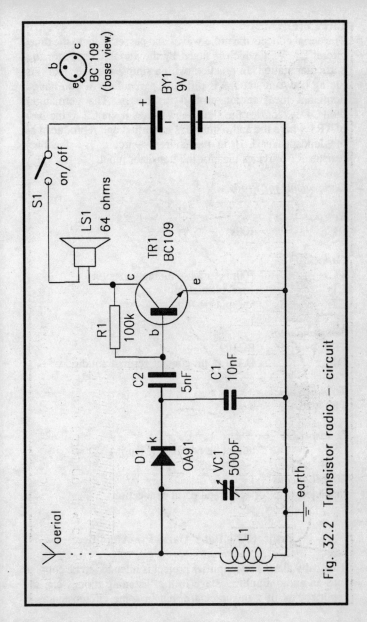

Fig. 32.2 Transistor radio — circuit

Circuit (Fig.32.2)

The aerial collects the radio waves and passes them to the tuned circuit L1, VC1 which is tuned by the variable capacitor to a particular station. In practice, with a simple receiver like this, tuning between stations is difficult, particularly if you have a dominant local station around the corner. The germanium diode, D1, rectifies the signal and passes it via C2 to the base of TR1 where the audio output is amplified and reproduced by the loudspeaker LS1 in the collector circuit. The feedback resistor R1 provides bias for the transistor input.

Components for Project 32

Resistor
R1   100k

Capacitors
VC1   500pF variable tuning capacitor
C1   10nF plastic foil
C2   5nF plastic foil

Semiconductors
TR1   BC109
D1   OA91 point-contact germanium diode

Terminal Block
TB1   9-way

Loudspeaker
LS1   miniature 64 ohms (Maplin)

Miscellaneous
Insulated wire for aerial and earth connections.

Project 33 – Baby Alarm Pre-Amplifier

This baby alarm pre-amplifier project is intended to be coupled into an audio amplifier stage in the 'listening room', e.g. the input socket of a music centre, but in some circumstances it

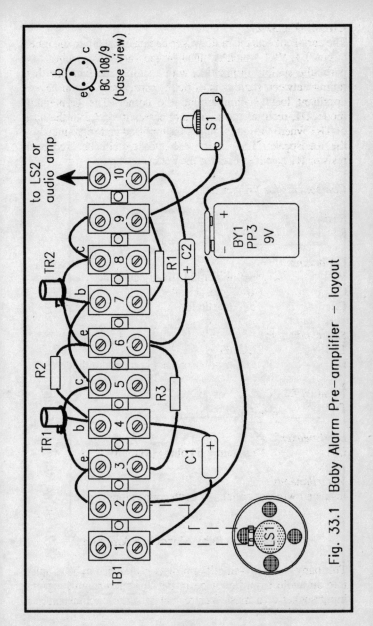

Fig. 33.1 Baby Alarm Pre-amplifier — layout

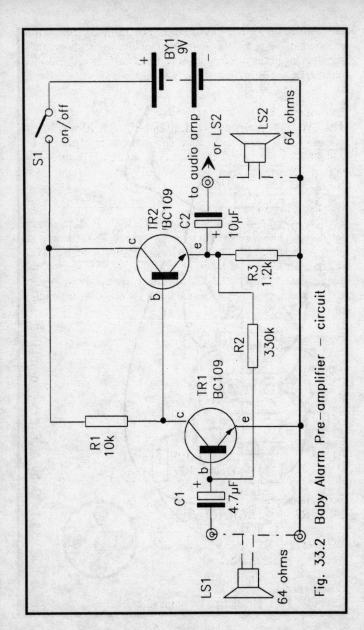

Fig. 33.2 Baby Alarm Pre-amplifier – circuit

124

could directly feed a loudspeaker. For instance, the output required depends on the sensitivity of the microphone/loudspeaker, the ambient noise level and that subjective factor, the number of decibels emitted by the infant in full cry.

Layout (Fig.33.1)

This two-stage pre-amplifier is assembled on a 10-way terminal block, TB1. If a long input lead is necessary from TB1.1 and TB1.2 connections, then screened audio cable should be used to prevent hum pick-up.

Circuit (Fig.33.2)

This two-stage high gain amplifier, TR1, TR2, is stabilised by feeding d.c. bias from R3 via R2 to the base of TR1. Direct coupling is employed from the collector of TR1 to the base of TR2, which reduces the number of components. As shown, the emitter-follower output via C2 can either be directly coupled to LS2 or plugged into an audio amplifier input socket depending on what volume is required.

Components for Project 33

Resistors

R1   10k
R2   330k
R3   1.2k

Capacitors

C1   4.7µF elect. 10V
C2   10µF elect. 10V

Semiconductors

TR1, TR2   BC109 (2 off)

Switches

S1   S.P.S.T.

Loudspeakers

LS1, LS2   miniature 64 ohms (2 off)

Terminal Block
TB1   10-way

Miscellaneous
Flat twin or audio cable, 9V battery and clip, etc.

Chapter 6

TEST AND MEASURING

When mechanical devices break down or need adjusting it's often possible to see what is wrong. In electronics a component rarely looks any different if it's faulty unless it has overheated. This final chapter offers an assortment of meters and testers that will help with trouble-shooting and measurement whether you are constructing projects or servicing equipment.

Project 34 – Continuity Tester

A continuity tester is often a handier service aid to carry around than a bulky multimeter. It can be made up into a pocket-size unit and comes in useful to check fuses, identify cable ends, the polarity of diodes, LEDs, transistor connections and to test printed-circuit boards, etc., for possible short-circuits.

Layout and Circuit (Fig.34.1)
The layout is simplicity itself, consisting of a 4-way terminal block to connect an LED, a resistor and a 3V battery (2 AA-type cells in a holder). The battery holder can be mounted on the back of the terminal block to make a compact unit.

The series circuit includes a current-limiting resistor R1, an LED D1, and a 3V battery BY1. The circuit is completed by the test probes. Most LEDs glow satisfactorily with a current of only 2 or 3mA, so circuits with resistances of several hundred ohms will still give an indication. The relative brightness of the LED will be proportional to the measure of continuity.

Components for Project 34

Resistor
R1   120 ohms

Semiconductor
D1   LED

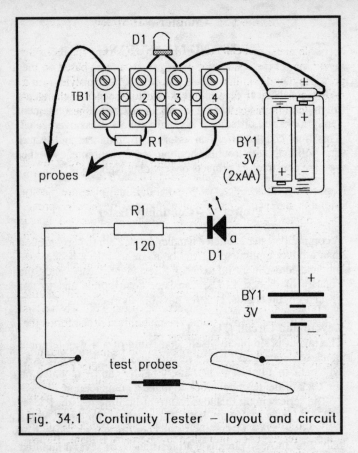

Fig. 34.1   Continuity Tester — layout and circuit

Terminal Block
TB1   4-way

Miscellaneous
3V battery (2 AA-type cells in holder) with clip, insulated leads
with probes or crocodile clips.

Project 35 – Moisture/pH Meter

A simple meter that can be switched to measuring the moisture in soil, or pH (percentage of hydrogen atoms), is based on the principle that dissimilar metals placed in an electrolyte form a simple cell. The voltage produced indicates whether the electrolyte (soil in this case) is acidic, neutral or alkaline.

Layout (Fig.35.1)

The meter probes of zinc, aluminium and copper are screwed into the terminal block connections TB1.1, TB1.2 and TB1.3 respectively. This copper wire and aluminium plate are readily available and a galvanised nail will serve for the zinc probe. The copper probe is connected to the negative (–) meter connection. The zinc probe and the aluminium probe are each connected to an outer contact of changeover switch S1. The wiper contact of S1 selects one of these and connects it to the positive (+) meter connection. The common copper probe to the meter (–) acts as the negative electrode of the 'cell' and the zinc probe forms the positive electrode of the 'cell' when S1 is switched to measure moisture. The aluminium probe forms the positive electrode when measuring pH.

For pH measurement, the probes should be inserted into previously moistened soil to take a reading. A pH meter reading of 7 indicates that the soil is neutral, neither alkaline nor acidic. Alkalinity is present in the soil if the reading is 7.5 or more; acidity is present for readings less than 5.5. For keen gardeners, more information is available on pH measurements in the author's recent book published by Bernard Babani, BP367, *Electronic Projects for the Garden.*

Components for Project 35

Meter
M1   250μA f.s.d. moving coil meter, order code LB80B, Maplin

Terminal Block
TB1   3-way

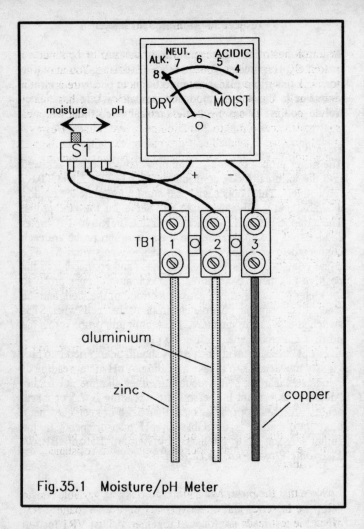

Fig.35.1 Moisture/pH Meter

Switch
S1   changeover, slider

Miscellaneous
Aluminium, copper and zinc probes (see text), wire links.

130

Project 36 – Simple Ohmmeter

A simple instrument for measuring resistance or continuity is extremely useful when you are project building. You may want to check to see if a fuse, light bulb filament or a wire is continuous, or to check the value of a resistance that has lost its colour-coding. This project offers a basic circuit that will measure resistance from 0 to 200 kilohms in two ranges. However, a higher range is available, if desired, as explained in the next paragraph. The meter used in the prototype was a moving coil signal strength meter with a full scale deflection (f.s.d.) of 250μA and an internal resistance of 625 ohms. The circuit is powered by 3V (two 1.5V AA-type cells in series in a battery holder). Resistance measurements must always be made with the equipment switched off.

Layout (Fig.36.1)
During construction, it is interesting to see how this ohmmeter can be further simplified to give an extended range up to 1 megohm, before adding the shunt arm, R1, R2, S1.

First take the terminal block, TB1, and proceed as follows:

- connect the –ve probe lead and the –ve of the meter M1 to TB1.1;
- connect the positive of the meter and one lead of VR1 to TB1.2;
- connect the other lead of VR1 and the +ve battery clip to TB1.5;
- connect the –ve battery clip and +ve probe lead to TB1.6;
- rotate VR1 fully anti-clockwise (maximum resistance) and fit battery.

Note that the meter M1 and the zero adjust variable resistor VR1 are in series and effectively across the 3V battery BY1 when the test leads are touched together. Adjust VR1 for full-scale deflection (the zero resistance measurement) on M1. A current of 250μA now flows through the circuit. By applying Ohm's Law the circuit resistance is calculated as 3V/250μA = 12 kilohms. If we now check a resistor of equal value (12k) across the test probes the current will be halved, and M1 will

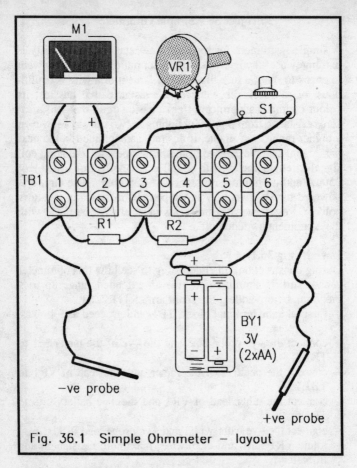

Fig. 36.1 Simple Ohmmeter – layout

register half-scale deflection (125µA). To obtain only slight deflection, say 3µA, the total resistance would need to be 3V/3µA = 1 megohm, so the circuit as it stands could be used for a 0–1 megohm range.

To complete the layout, add resistors R1 and R2 and the range switch S1.

One end of R1 can be temporarily disconnected (or switched) if a high resistance value, say from 200k to 1M, is to be measured.

132

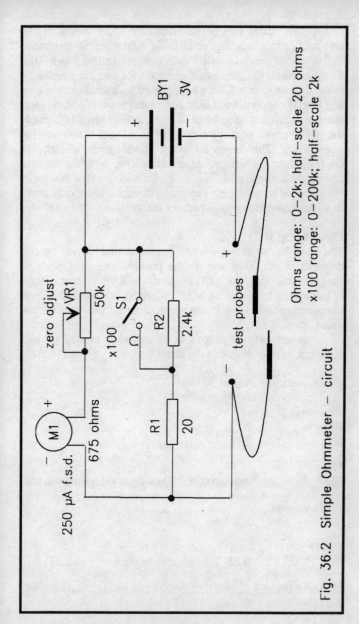

Fig. 36.2 Simple Ohmmeter – circuit

Ohms range: 0–2k; half-scale 20 ohms
x100 range: 0–200k; half-scale 2k

Separate scales can be calibrated by using precision test resistors, or by comparing results with a commercial test meter.

The components fit easily on a 6-way terminal block TB1. The meter M1, the zero adjust control VR1 and the pushbutton range change switch S1 can be mounted on a small plastic project box. If copper wire is used for instrument test probes, insulated sleeving should be fitted to prevent short-circuits. Identify the positive and negative probes with red and black sleeving respectively. This is useful when checking the polarity of diodes; when the test probes are connected with the positive one on the cathode end (indicated by a wide band) a low resistance should be indicated. Reversing the test leads should result in a high resistance reading across the diode.

Circuit (Fig.36.2)

The basic circuit shows the two ranges available with the two resistors in the shunt arm. In the position indicated, with S1 range switch open, the ×100 range (0–200k) is selected, largely influenced by the value of R2. When S1 is closed, the lower ohms range (0–2k) is selected and resistor R1 provides the low value shunt.

As mentioned, the range can be extended to read up to 1 megohm by disconnecting the shunt arm, e.g. one end of R1.

Components for Project 36

Resistors
R1   20
R2   2.4k

Meter
M1   moving coil, 250µA f.s.d. (Maplin – see text)

Potentiometer
VR1   50k Lin

Switch
S1   S.P.S.T. or push-to-make

Terminal Block
TB1   6-way

Miscellaneous
AA-type 1.5V batteries (2 off) with battery box and clip, stranded wire cable and probes.

Project 37 – 1V/10V Voltmeter

Normally, the measurement of volts, amps and ohms could easily be incorporated in one multimeter project, but for simplicity in our terminal block projects, they are considered as separate projects. Also, as all the projects in this book are powered from low voltage, direct current (d.c.) sources, it was decided to limit the upper range to 10V d.c. The lower range, 0 to 1V, is particularly useful for checking emitter-base voltages on transistors, which need to be approximately 0.7V or above for conduction.

As in the previous project, the meter is a 250µA moving coil type with an internal resistance of 625 ohms. However, if available, a 100µA will give greater accuracy, as it imposes less load on the circuit under test.

Layout (Fig.37.1)
The layout uses a six-way terminal block TB1 and is self-explanatory. The few components can be screwed to a plywood base or fitted in a small project box, as desired.

Again, the scales can be calibrated by using known voltages or by comparing results with an accurate voltmeter.

Circuit (Fig.37.2)
The variable resistor VR1 provides an adjustment for the low range (0–1V). Range switch S1 should be closed, i.e. only the series multiplier R1 in circuit, to make this adjustment. With S1 released, both R1 and R2 act as series multipliers for the 0–10V range.

IMPORTANT NOTE: On no account connect the meter to any voltage source greater than 10V. Never, ever attempt to use the meter with mains or any other high voltage sources.

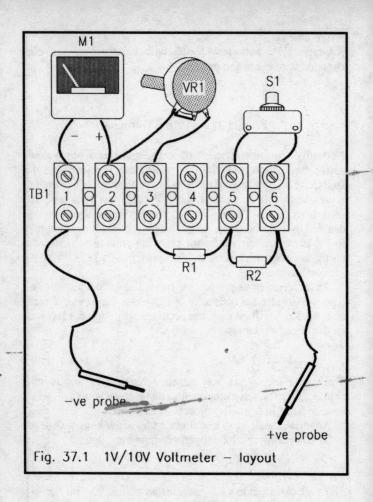

Fig. 37.1   1V/10V Voltmeter — layout

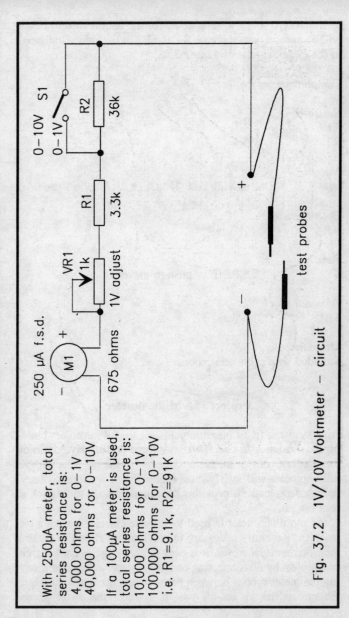

With 250µA meter, total
series resistance is:
4,000 ohms for 0–1V
40,000 ohms for 0–10V

If a 100µA meter is used,
total series resistance is:
10,000 ohms for 0–1V
100,000 ohms for 0–10V
i.e. R1=9.1k, R2=91K

250 µA f.s.d.

M1

VR1
1k
1V adjust

675 ohms

R1
3.3k

0–10V S1
0–1V

R2
36k

test probes

Fig. 37.2 1V/10V Voltmeter – circuit

137

If a 100μA meter is substituted for the 250μA meter, then it will be necessary to increase R1 and R2 to the values indicated in the marginal note on Figure 37.2.

Components for Project 37

Resistors
R1   3.3k
R2   36k

Meter
M1   moving coil, 250μA f.s.d. (Maplin – see text)

Potentiometer
VR1   1k Lin

Switch
S1   S.P.S.T. or push-to-make

Terminal Block
TB1   6-way

Miscellaneous
Stranded wire cable and probes.

Project 38 – Milliammeter

Direct current (d.c.) measurements are useful in project building, for instance to check whether there is excessive drain on the battery, or to measure collector current. This simple milliammeter will satisfy most requirements for these battery-operated projects. It provides measurements up to 250mA in four ranges.

As a milliammeter is used to indicate current flow in a circuit, it is generally necessary to break into a circuit to make a measurement. However, it is easy to check the overall current in a project by disconnecting one of the battery clips and inserting the meter probes between battery and clip. Alternatively, if the circuit has an on–off switch, connect the meter probes

138

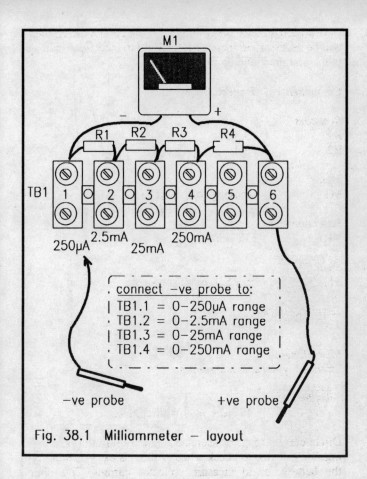

Fig. 38.1 Milliammeter – layout

across it on the 'off' position. For correct polarity, the +ve
probe should always be towards the positive battery terminal.

Layout (Fig.38.1)
The universal shunt resistors and the meter are all wired on one
side of the 6-way terminal block TB1 to leave the other side
free for the probes. To simplify the circuit, the –ve probe is
moved to the appropriate terminal block position, TB1.1–4,

139

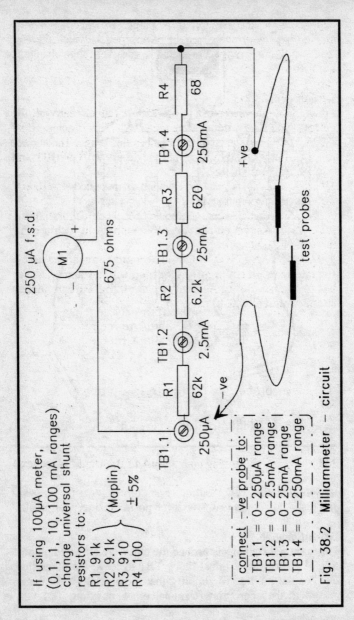

Fig. 38.2 Milliammeter — circuit

250 μA f.s.d.

M1

675 ohms

If using 100μA meter,
(0.1, 1, 10, 100 mA ranges)
change universal shunt
resistors to:
R1 91k
R2 9.1k   (Maplin)
R3 910   ± 5%
R4 100

R1 62k
R2 6.2k
R3 620
R4 68

TB1.1 250μA
TB1.2 2.5mA
TB1.3 25mA
TB1.4 250mA

test probes

+ve

−ve

connect −ve probe to:
TB1.1 = 0−250μA range
TB1.2 = 0−2.5mA range
TB1.3 = 0−25mA range
TB1.4 = 0−250mA range

depending on the required mA range. However, a 4-way, single-pole rotary switch could be inserted between the −ve lead and the four range terminals if a speedier range change is required.

Circuit (Fig.38.2)

For accurate measurement in the 250µA range, nearly all the current should flow through the meter M1. This is achieved by the high total resistance of the shunt in this range. The current ratios that are passed by the other ranges are 9:10, 99:100, and 999:1000 approximately.

The shunt values must be changed as indicated if a 100µA meter is substituted for M1.

Any inaccuracies can be allowed for when calibrating the scale, using known currents and by comparison with a commercial milliammeter.

IMPORTANT NOTE: On no account connect the meter to mains equipment or any other high voltage source. Never use this piece of equipment on anything with a higher supply voltage than 10V.

Components for Project 38

Resistors

R1	62k	
R2	6.2k	± 5% (Maplin)
R3	620	
R4	68	

Meter
M1   moving coil, 250µA f.s.d. (Maplin – see text)

Terminal Block
TB1   6-way

Miscellaneous
Stranded wire cable and probes.

Project 39 – Transistor Tester

This simple project offers a means of testing silicon npn transistors, e.g. the general-purpose BC109 used in many of these terminal block projects. Although not a comprehensive test, it checks for leakage, and gives an indication of the current gain of a transistor by measuring the current in its collector circuit.

Layout (Fig.39.1)
The wiring of the 6-way terminal block TB1 is arranged so that three connectors are left free to screw in the transistor on test. Three small socket connectors could be fitted if batch testing in quantities is envisaged. With a little dexterity, testing can also be speeded up by simply touching the legs of the transistor on the three adjacent screw heads of the terminals (TB1.4–6) and pressing S1.

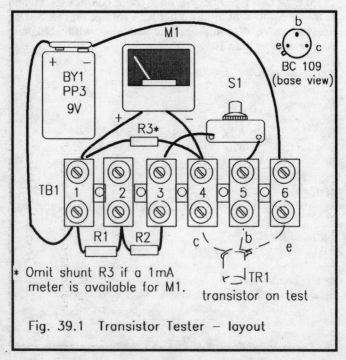

Fig. 39.1 Transistor Tester – layout

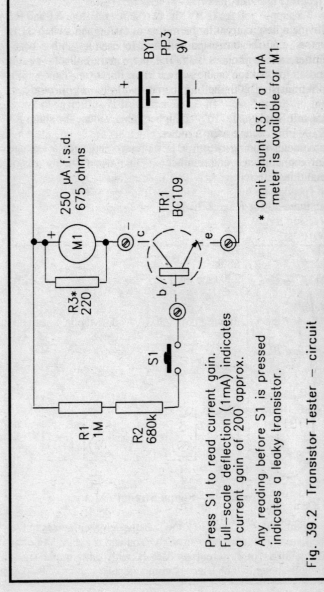

Press S1 to read current gain.
Full-scale deflection (1mA) indicates
a current gain of 200 approx.

Any reading before S1 is pressed
indicates a leaky transistor.

Fig. 39.2 Transistor Tester – circuit

* Omit shunt R3 if a 1mA
  meter is available for M1.

250 µA f.s.d.
675 ohms

M1

+   —

R3*
220

TR1
BC109

c

b

e

S1

R1
1M

R2
680k

BY1
PP3
9V

+   —

Circuit (Fig.39.2)

With a supply voltage of 9V, the two series resistors R1 and R2 provide a base current in the region of 5μA when switch S1 is pressed, and the transistor will start to conduct with a base-emitter voltage of about 0.7V. The meter in the collector circuit reads in proportion to the current gain. For a transistor with a current gain of 200, the base current will give a collector current of $200 \times 5\mu A = 1mA$. Generally, it is sufficient to know that gain is adequate. To read higher gains, reduce the shunt R3 to 100 ohms or use a 2mA meter.

A meter reading before M1 is pressed indicates a leakage between collector and emitter. In this event the transistor should be rejected.

Components for Project 39

Resistors

R1	1M
R2	680k
R3	220 (see text)

Meter

M1	moving coil, 250μA f.s.d. (Maplin – see text)

Terminal Block

TB1	6-way

Miscellaneous
9V PP3 battery with clip.

Project 40 – Signal Strength Meter

Sometimes it is difficult to know whether an oscillator is in fact oscillating and if so, how strongly. You can measure and compare outputs of different oscillators with this simple signal strength meter, which uses six components.

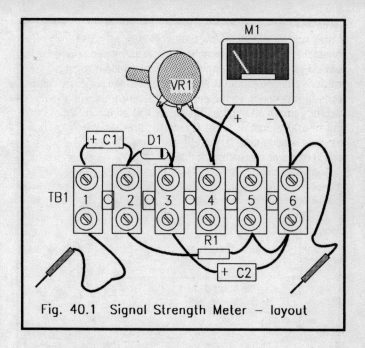

Fig. 40.1 Signal Strength Meter — layout

Layout (Fig.40.1)

The wiring of the 6-way terminal block TB1 includes a short
wire link to avoid more than two leads to each terminal screw.
It also means that component spans along the terminal block
are reduced. Make sure that the germanium diode D1, the two
electrolytic capacitors C1, C2, and the meter M1 are connected
the right way round.

Circuit (Fig.40.2)

The alternating current produced by an oscillator, or tone generator, is sampled by this circuit, rectified and the d.c. output is
measured on the meter. The capacitor C1 blocks any d.c. input,
but passes any alternating waveforms speech or continuous
tone signals to the anode of the diode D1. As current can only
flow in one direction through a diode, D1 will only conduct
when its anode is more positive than its cathode. A germanium
diode is used because it is sensitive; it starts to conduct when

145

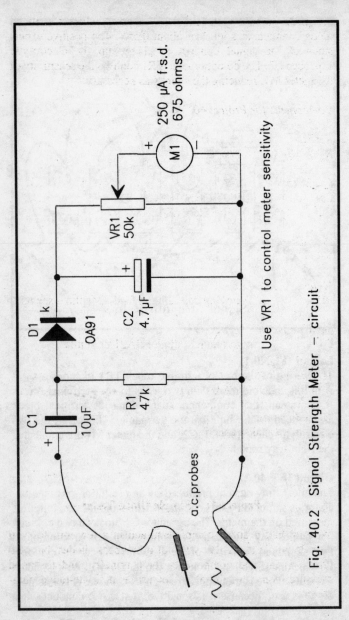

250 µA f.s.d.
675 ohms

M1

VR1
50k

Use VR1 to control meter sensitivity

D1
k
OA91

C2
4.7µF

R1
47k

C1
10µF

a.c. probes

Fig. 40.2 Signal Strength Meter – circuit

the anode–cathode voltage is 0.15V approx., whereas a silicon diode conducts at a level of about 0.55V. The positive excursions of the signal conduct to charge up the electrolytic capacitor C2. The potentiometer VR1 controls the sensitivity of the meter M1, reducing the swings as necessary.

Components for Project 40

Resistor
R1   47k

Capacitors
C1   10µF elect. 10V
C2   4.7µF elect. 10V

Potentiometer
VR1   50k Lin

Meter
M1   moving coil, 250µA f.s.d. (Maplin – see text)

Semiconductor
D1   germanium diode, OA91 or similar

Terminal Block
TB1   6-way

Miscellaneous
Test probes and stranded cable.

Project 41 – Simple Diode Tester

Wire up half a dozen components and in a few minutes you have a simple tester that will not only check diodes, but also check wiring and components for continuity; and for good measure, you can calibrate it for use as a single-range ohm-meter.

Layout (Fig.41.1)

There's plenty of room on the 6-way terminal block TB1 for the half dozen components, as the suggested layout shows. If this is intended as a permanent piece of test equipment it is best mounted in a small project box. When used as a free-standing test meter, switch S1 could be omitted and a link inserted in its place as no current flows in the circuit unless the probes are connected.

Circuit (Fig.41.2)

This simple series circuit needs little explanation. Resistor R1 acts as a current limiter to prevent the meter needle wrapping itself around the end stop if the zero adjust resistor VR1 happens to be set at the low resistance end. The two AA-type cells should not need to be replaced very often because the maximum current never exceeds $250\mu A$. As the battery voltage drops, the VR1 setting should be gradually reduced with the probes shorted together to restore the full-scale reading.

Diode Testing

Before making any checks, connect the two probes together and adjust the variable resistor (VR1) for maximum reading on the meter, i.e. full-scale deflection. In ohmic measurements, this reading represents zero ohms. Remember that diodes are one-way conductors; they pass current easily in one direction (from anode to cathode) but not in the other direction. Applying the test probes across the ends of the diode in one direction should give almost full-scale deflection, and practically no reading when the probes are reversed. The cathode end of a diode is usually marked with a band. However, this is easily identified by connecting the test probes to the two ends. When the meter reading is almost full-scale, the end in contact with the +ve test probe is the cathode. A low reading in both directions indicates a faulty diode.

Continuity and Ohmic Testing

The total resistance of the circuit will be $V/R = 3V/250\mu A = 12k$ for the zero adjust reading (i.e. full-scale deflection at $250\mu A$) when the probes are shorted together or, for instance, checking for continuity in a length of wire. As explained in the

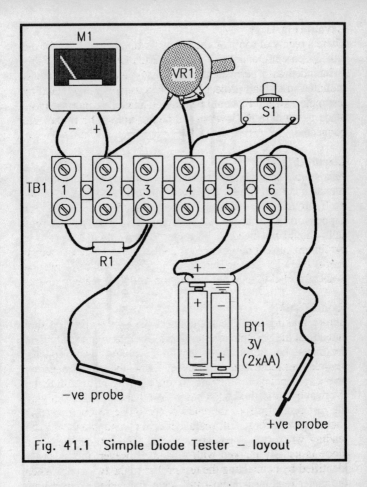

Fig. 41.1 Simple Diode Tester — layout

ohmmeter project, including an external 12k resistor in circuit for measurement would give a half-scale reading. The scale will be cramped at the left-hand side, but by applying Ohm's Law, we can see that a deflection of $10\mu A$, a 25th of the scale, would indicate a series resistance of $V/R = 3V/10\mu A = 330k$. This high resistance range is a useful bonus and the scale could easily be calibrated up to say 500k by checking some known resistor values at intervals over this range.

149

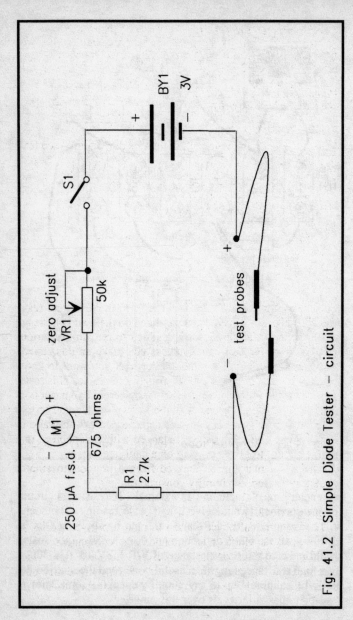

Fig. 41.2 Simple Diode Tester – circuit

150

Components for Project 41

Resistor
R1   2.7k

Potentiometer
VR1   50k Lin

Meter
M1   moving coil, 250µA f.s.d. (Maplin – see text)

Terminal Block
TB1   6-way

Miscellaneous
Test probes and stranded cable.
3V battery (2AA-type cells in holder) with clip

Project 42 – Capacitance Tester

Capacitors are generally more difficult to identify than resistors, although some have values marked on them and others are colour-coded. Many others are destined to remain mysterious blobs of wax, mica or plastic unless you make up this capacitance tester. Usually, for most applications you want to know whether a capacitor is good and roughly its value. This tester applied an a.c. signal of several kilohertz across two capacitors in series; the capacitor on test and a known capacitor. The two voltages appearing across the two capacitors are in the ratio of their values. This ratio can be balanced with headphones, in a bridge circuit, to give a reading on a calibrated scale.

The a.c. signal can be derived from a previous oscillator circuit, if desired, to simplify construction.

Layout (Fig.42.1)
A 12-way terminal block is used to reduce over-crowding. In this project, sleeving is recommended over component ends to avoid short-circuits at the cross-overs. To save time when batch-testing, the capacitors on test can be more easily connected by two wire-ended crocodile clips attached to TB1.11 and TB1.12.

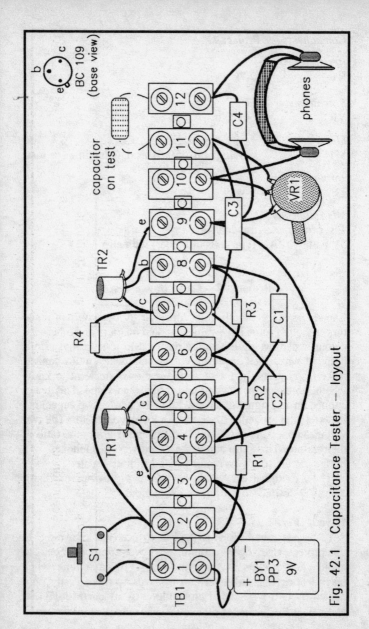

Fig. 42.1 Capacitance Tester – layout

152

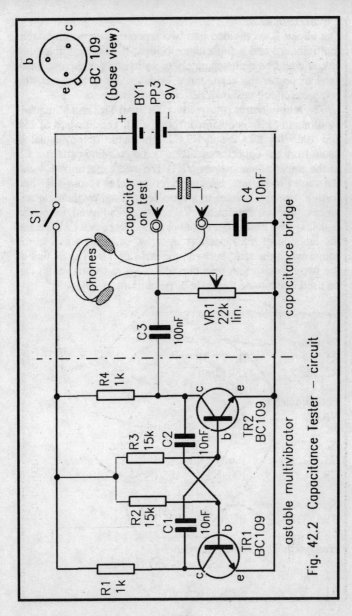

Fig. 42.2 Capacitance Tester — circuit

BC 109 (base view)

BY1
PP3
9V

S1

capacitor on test

phones

C3 100nF

VR1 22k lin.

C4 10nF

capacitance bridge

R4 1k

R3 15k

C2 10nF

TR2 BC109

R2 15k

C1 10nF

TR1 BC109

R1 1k

astable multivibrator

Circuit (Fig.42.2)

The circuit is subdivided into two separate circuits: an astable multivibrator and a capacitance bridge. If desired, the astable circuit could be built separately or an existing audio oscillator used to power the capacitance bridge section. However, the complete circuit is shown here for convenience.

The multivibrator is formed by TR1 and TR2 and a frequency of about 5kHz is obtained from the RC combination of 15k and 10nF for R2,C2 and R3,C1. The audio output signal is taken from the collector of TR2, via the coupling capacitor C3 to the linear potentiometer VR1. The two capacitors, C4 and the capacitor on test, are connected in series across VR1 and form a potential divider in a ratio determined by their capacitances. The potentiometer VR1 can be adjusted to obtain balance. The headphones connected between VR1 slider and the junction of the capacitors in series will give a null in the sound when the ratio between the arms of VR1 equals that of the two capacitors. A selection of known capacitor values can be used to calibrate the scale of potentiometer VR1.

Components for Project 42

Resistors
R1, R4   1k (2 off)
R2, R3   15k (2 off)

Potentiometer
VR1   22k Lin

Capacitors
C1, C2, C4   10nF (3 off)
C3   100nF

Semiconductors
TR1, TR2   BC109 (2 off)

Headphones   High impedance

Switch
S1   S.P.S.T. (on/off)

Terminal Block
TB1   12-way

Miscellaneous
9V battery PP3 and clip, wire links.

Project 43 – Simple Thermometer

Thermistors are resistors that are temperature conscious. Warm them up or cool them down and they change value considerably, which makes them very useful for sensing temperature changes. The type used here for measuring temperature is a negative temperature coefficient (n.t.c.) thermistor, one that decreases in resistance as it gets hotter, although positive temperature coefficient (p.t.c.) thermistors are available for other applications such as over-current protection.

Layout (Fig.43.1)
There are only five components, and a 5-way terminal block suffices. The thermistor Th1 leads can be extended by an additional 2-way block if it is used to sense temperatures at some distance from the measuring circuit, e.g. for external temperature readings. Make sure that the leads to the thermistor are well-insulated, as any moisture between them will produce some conductivity. This will effectively be in parallel with the thermistor, lowering the overall resistance and giving a reading error.

Circuit (Fig.43.2)
The diagram shows a simple series circuit with a 3V battery producing a current through the thermistor Th1, which is read on a microammeter M1. A variable resistor VR1 in series is adjusted to give full-scale deflection at 100 deg. C. Some calibration points are given as a guide, and intermediate points can easily be worked out from these, or by comparison with a standard thermometer.

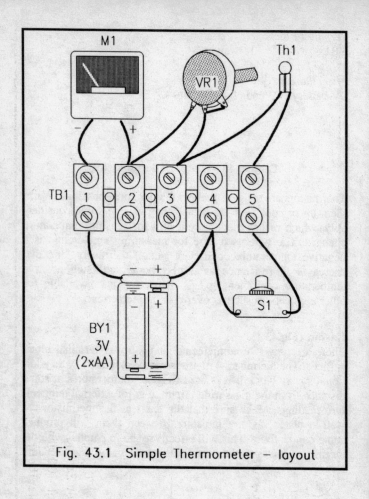

Fig. 43.1   Simple Thermometer – layout

Components for Project 43

Potentiometer
VR1   22k Lin

Meter
M1   250µA

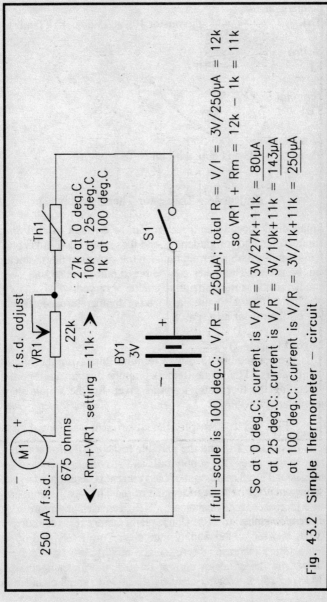

M1
− +
250 µA f.s.d.

675 ohms
← Rm+VR1 setting = 11k →

f.s.d. adjust

VR1
22k

Th1

27k at 0 deg.C
10k at 25 deg.C
1k at 100 deg.C

BY1
3V
+
−

S1

If full-scale is 100 deg.C: V/R = 250µA; total R = V/I = 3V/250µA = 12k
so VR1 + Rm = 12k − 1k = 11k

So at 0 deg.C: current is V/R = 3V/27k+11k = 80µA
at 25 deg.C: current is V/R = 3V/10k+11k = 143µA
at 100 deg.C: current is V/R = 3V/1k+11k = 250µA

Fig. 43.2 Simple Thermometer − circuit

157

Semiconductor
Th1   n.t.c. thermistor 10k at 25 deg. C. (Tandy)

Switch
S1   S.P.S.T.

Terminal Block
TB1   5-way

Miscellaneous
9V battery PP3 and clip, wire links.

Project 44 – Transistor Thermometer

Small differences in temperature can be difficult to read on a small meter, and for gardeners, and those interested in keeping temperatures within certain limits, a transistorised thermometer can be useful. The meter can be set to mid-scale so that even small variations in temperature can be observed.

This project also uses a negative temperature coefficient (n.t.c.) thermistor as a sensor.

Layout (Fig.44.1)
This project requires a 6-way terminal block for the circuit components. The same remarks apply for insulating and extending the thermistor leads as given for the simple thermometer (Project 43).

Circuit (Fig.44.2)
The thermistor Th1 and the variable resistor VR1 form a voltage divider across the supply rails and provide base current for transistor TR1. The amount of base current is determined by the setting of VR1 and the resistance of the Th1. As the temperature increases, the resistance of Th1 decreases and more base current is applied to TR1. Consequently, more collector current flows and the meter reading increases. Conversely, a drop in temperature increases the resistance of Th1, less base current flows and the collector current through the meter decreases. The 0 to 250 microamp meter is sensitive to small changes in

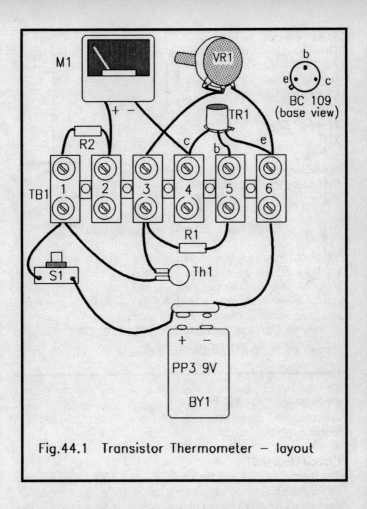

Fig.44.1 Transistor Thermometer — layout

temperature. To cover a wider range of temperature, a 0 to 1 milliamp meter could be substituted, if desired. Remember that you can increase the range of the 250 microamp meter by connecting a shunt resistor across its terminals; try a 200 ohm resistor between TB1.2 and TB1.4 to make the meter less sensitive.

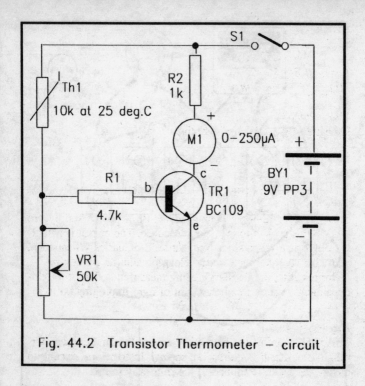

Fig. 44.2 Transistor Thermometer — circuit

Components for Project 44

Resistors
R1   4.7k
R2   1k

Potentiometer
VR1   50k Lin

Meter
M1   250µA

Semiconductors
TR1   BC109
Th1   n.t.c. thermistor 10k at 25 deg. C (Tandy)

Switch
S1   S.P.S.T.

Terminal Block
TB1   6-way

Miscellaneous
9V battery PP3 and clip, wire links.

Project 45 – Light Meter

Two potential dividers connected across a power supply are
used in this project to measure resistance. The circuit is actual-
ly known as a Wheatstone bridge after Sir Charles Wheatstone,
who also invented the electric telegraph and the concertina.

In this case, the resistance being measured is that of a light-
dependent resistor, i.e. the amount of light impinging on it.

Layout (Fig.45.1)
This simple circuit can be quickly assembled on the 6-way terminal block and requires no special instructions except to
ensure the meter is connected the right way round.

Circuit (Fig.45.2)
When switch S1 is on, current will flow in both arms of the
bridge. If the resistance ratio of PCC1 to VR1 is equal to the
ratio of R1 to R2 then the bridge will be balanced and the meter
will read zero, i.e. no current will flow through the meter.
Variable resistor VR1 can be adjusted at a low light level for
this condition. When PCC1, the photo-cell is gradually exposed
to light its resistance will gradually decrease so that VR1 gets
a greater share of the potential across the PCC1, VR1 arm of
the bridge. Consequently, the bridge is now unbalanced and
current flows from the positive terminal of the battery via
PCC1 through the meter and via R2 to the negative terminal of
the battery. The meter indication is a measure of the light
falling on PCC1.

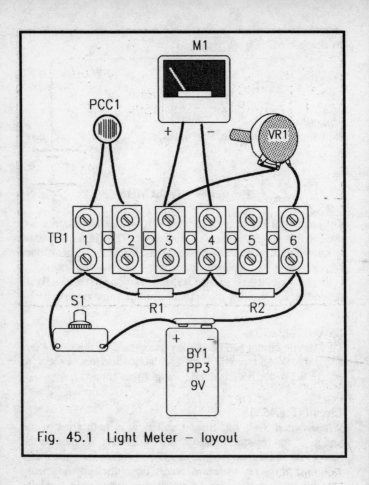

Fig. 45.1 Light Meter — layout

Components for Project 45

Resistors
R1   150k
R2   4.7k

Potentiometer
VR1   22k Lin

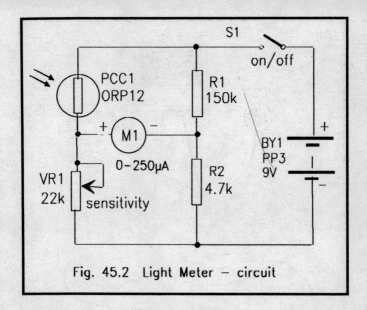

Fig. 45.2 Light Meter — circuit

Meter
M1   250µA

Semiconductors
PCC1   ORP12

Switch
S1   S.P.S.T.

Terminal Block
TB1   6-way

Miscellaneous
9V battery PP3 and clip, wire links.